Exploring Science 8

Mark Levesley
Sandra Baggley
Julian Clarke
Steve Gray
Penny Johnson

Additional material by
Andrea Coates

PEARSON
Longman

Edinburgh Gate
Harlow, Essex

Contents

What does our food contain?

In science, the word **diet** means 'what you eat'. Your food is a source of **raw materials** for your body. These raw materials are needed to make new substances for:
- energy (to help us move, etc.)
- growth and repair
- health.

1 What do scientists mean by the word 'diet'?

2 Give one reason why we need energy from our food.

Many foods have **nutrition information** labels which tell you what is in them. If you look at the left-hand column of the table you will see the names of the different things in the food. Apart from energy, which is not a substance, the other parts of the food are all substances which your body needs.

Use this column to compare foods.

BREAD 800 g ⓔ		
NUTRITION		
TYPICAL COMPOSITON	A 200g serving provides	100g provide
Energy	1840 kJ	920 kJ
Protein	20.6 g	10.3 g
Carbohydrate	76.8 g	38.4 g
Fat	5.0 g	2.5 g
Fibre	13.0 g	6.5 g
VITAMINS		
Thiamin	0.6 mg (42% RDA)	0.3 mg (21% RDA)
Niacin	8.2 mg (44% RDA)	4.1 mg (22% RDA)
Folic acid	78.0 µg (39% RDA)	39.0 µg (19% RDA)
MINERALS		
Iron	5.4 mg (38% RDA)	2.7 mg (19% RDA)
Sodium	1.0 g	0.5 g
RDA = recommended daily allowance		
INFORMATION		

3 a) Look at the bread nutrition information label on the right. Six types of food substances are shown. What are they?
b) If you add up the masses of each food substance in the right-hand column, they do not add up to 100 g as you would expect. The rest of the mass of the food comes from the water it contains. Ignoring the tiny values for vitamins and minerals, work out how much water there is in 100 g of the bread.
c) Name the *five* types of food substance that make up most of the bread.

Nutrition information from a loaf of wholemeal bread. (1 mg = 0.001 g; 1 µg = 0.000001 g).

Carbohydrates, fats, proteins, vitamins and minerals are all **nutrients**. Nutrients are substances which provide raw materials for the body. We also need **fibre** and **water** in our diet.

Fibre is made of plant cell walls. Our bodies cannot use it but eating it helps to keep our intestines clean and healthy. It also stops our intestines getting blocked up (**constipation**). A good source of fibre is wholemeal bread.

4 You are in charge of marketing a new breakfast cereal called FullBran, which contains a lot of fibre. Write down a slogan you would use for a newspaper advertisement.

About 65% of your body is made out of water. Water is an important **solvent** in the body (it dissolves things so that they can be carried around the body). It is also used to fill up cells so that they can hold their shapes. Water can also help to cool you down when you sweat. A very small amount of water is used as a raw material for making things in your body but it is not often thought of as a nutrient. You must drink lots of water each day to stay healthy.

5 a) Which substances in food are called nutrients?
b) What other substances do you need in your diet?
c) What are these substances needed for?

People can sometimes survive for over 60 days without food but only a few days without water.

P We can find out which nutrients a food contains by testing it.

 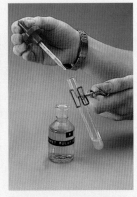 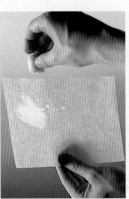

Starch *is a type of carbohydrate. The test for starch: Add two drops of iodine solution to a food sample. If starch is there you will see a blue/black colour.*

*The test for **protein**: Place a food sample in a test tube to a depth of about 1 cm. Add five drops of Biuret solution. If there is protein you will see a purple colour but this may take a few minutes to appear.*

*The test for **fat**: Rub a small dry food sample on some white paper. Hold the paper up to the light. Fat will leave a greasy mark.*

How would you test these foods to see which nutrients they contained? (The tests for starch and protein need the food sample to be mixed with an equal volume of water.)

6 Gita was making herself some wholemeal bread and butter. She decided to test the butter and the bread with iodine. Which nutrient was she testing for?

7 a) Sugars are a type of carbohydrate. You can also do food tests for sugars. Which of these foods do you think will have a lot of sugar in them?
fish   fizzy drink   potato   chocolate   sausages
b) Name one other sort of carbohydrate.

You should know...

● **What food is needed for.**

● **The names of the nutrients found in food.**

● **Why water and fibre are also needed in our diets.**

What is a balanced diet?

Different foods contain different substances. There is no one food that contains all the substances that you need. You need to eat a wide variety of foods. This is called having a **balanced diet**.

In Alberta, Canada, mountain lambs have been dying. The adult sheep prefer sweets and hamburgers, fed to them by tourists, rather than grass. The junk food is not a balanced diet for the sheep and the ewes do not produce enough milk to feed their lambs.

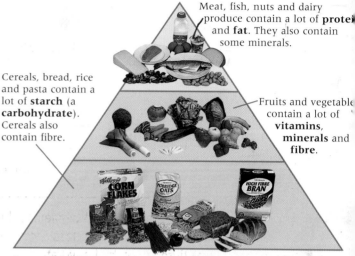

Meat, fish, nuts and dairy produce contain a lot of **protei** and **fat**. They also contain some minerals.

Cereals, bread, rice and pasta contain a lot of **starch** (a **carbohydrate**). Cereals also contain fibre.

Fruits and vegetable contain a lot of **vitamins**, **minerals** and **fibre**.

To get a balanced diet, people should eat food from each of these groups every day. People should aim to eat more from the groups lower in the triangle.

Food substances for energy

Carbohydrates are good sources of energy. Starch and sugar are two kinds of carbohydrate. **Starch** is found in foods like bread, rice, pasta and potatoes. **Sugars** are found in many foods (including sweets and cakes).

When carbohydrates are not used up, they can be turned into fat in your body. **Fats** are also found in foods like milk, cheese, butter and eggs. Fat is stored in your body to be used for energy in the future. Some fat is stored under your skin to help stop heat escaping from your body.

Different people need different amounts of food. You need more food if you are very active and you need more food if you are a boy. The amount of **chemical energy** that a food contains is measured in **kilojoules** (kJ). If you look at the left-hand column of the table at the top of page 7 you will see the names of the different things in the food. Apart from energy, which is not a substance, the other parts of the food are all substances which your body needs.

Marathon runners often pick up drinks containing a sugar called glucose during their run.

1 What is a balanced diet?

2 a) Starch and sugar are two examples of a particular food substance. Which food substance?
   b) Name two sources of starch.
   c) Name two sources of sugar.

3 How is fat used in the body?

	Recommended amount for boys each day	Recommended amount for girls each day	100 g of milk contain	100 g of eggs contain	100 g of wholemeal bread contain	100 g of chips contain	100 g of oranges contain	100 g of butter contain	100 g of chocolate contain
Energy	11 700 kJ	9600 kJ	274 kJ	612 kJ	920 kJ	1028 kJ	150 kJ	3000 kJ	2411 kJ
Carbohydrate	350 g	300 g	4.8 g	0 g	38.4 g	37.3 g	8.5 g	0 g	54.5 g
Protein	50–100 g	50–90 g	3.3 g	12.3 g	10.3 g	3.8 g	0.8 g	0.5 g	8.7 g
Fat	70–100 g	60–90 g	3.8 g	10.9 g	2.5 g	9 g	0 g	81 g	37.6 g
Fibre	30 g	30 g	0 g	0 g	6.5 g	2 g	2.1 g	0 g	0 g
Vitamin C	25 mg	25 mg	1 mg	0 mg	0 mg	6 mg	50 mg	0 mg	0 mg
Vitamin D	2.5 µg	2.5 µg	0.05 µg	1.5 µg	0 µg	0 µg	0 µg	13 µg	0 µg
Calcium	700 mg	700 mg	120 mg	54 mg	28 mg	14 mg	41 mg	15 mg	246 mg
Iron	14 mg	14 mg	0.1 mg	2.1 mg	3 mg	1.4 mg	0.3 mg	0.2 mg	1.7 mg

The recommended amounts are approximate and depend on your age and how active you are.

4 Look at the table. One thick slice of wholemeal bread has a mass of 50 g. How much of the following does it contain?
a) protein   b) fibre   c) carbohydrate

5 a) A 50 g slice of wholemeal bread is spread with 10 g of butter. How much chemical energy is in this snack?
b) If this snack was tested using iodine solution, what would the result be? (*Hint*: You may need to look back to page 5.)

Body builders eat a lot of protein. They often take special foods which give them extra protein.

Food substances for growth and repair

Proteins are needed to make new cells to help us grow and to repair our bodies. Proteins are found in foods like meat, fish, eggs, cheese, beans and milk.

6 a) Name two sources of protein.
b) Why do you need proteins in your diet?

Some people worry that they do not get enough vitamins and minerals in their diet. They may take tablets containing vitamins and minerals. However, taking too much of a particular vitamin can be harmful.

Food substances for health

Vitamins and **mineral salts** (often just called **minerals**) are needed in small quantities. They are often found in fruits and vegetables. They help to keep our bodies healthy.

7 a) How many grams of oranges would you need to get the recommended amount of:
i) vitamin C   ii) iron?
b) Which food in the table is the best source of iron?

8 a) Draw a food chain to show cows, grass and humans.
b) How is the diet of cows different to humans?
c) Find out why humans do not eat grass.

9 Do you think you eat a balanced diet? Explain your reasoning.

You should know...
- **What a balanced diet is.**
- **Why we need carbohydrates, fats, proteins, vitamins and minerals in our diets.**
- **Which foods these substances are found in.**

What problems can diets cause?

It does not matter exactly what you eat as long as you eat a balanced diet. The photographs on the right show typical foods eaten by people in different parts of the world every day.

A meal from the UK.

A meal from Italy.

A meal from India.

 1 Each of the photographs shows a balanced diet. Explain why.

In some parts of the world, people cannot get enough to eat and they starve. In other areas people get diseases caused by a lack of a nutrient.

We may not like the idea but insects are eaten by many people all over the world. Roasted grasshoppers are a delicacy in Mexico. They are served with mashed avocado on a tortilla.

In the UK, many people are concerned about eating too much fat. Scientists think that eating too much fat can cause **heart disease**. Eating too much fat or sugar can also make you fat (extra sugar is turned into fat in the body).

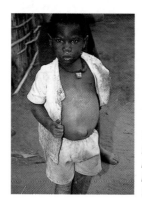
This child is suffering from a disease called kwashiorkor, caused by a lack of protein in the diet.

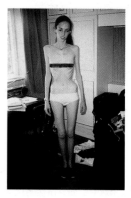
This person has anorexia.

Some people go on diets that make them ill because the diets are not balanced or contain too little food. People who do not eat enough often feel weak and tired. In some cases this can lead to a disease called anorexia.

To stay healthy you have to keep the balance right and eat a wide range of foods which contain all the nutrients you need.

 2 Look at the picture of the roasted grasshoppers. Which nutrient would the following parts contain a lot of?
a) the tortilla (made from flour) b) the grasshoppers

3 What is kwashiorkor?

4 Some people try to eat no fat. Why do you think doctors advise against this?

5 Do you think small children and adults should have the same diets? Explain your reasoning.

You should know...

● Too much or too little of certain food substances can cause diseases.

Why do some people have to avoid eating certain foods?

People with **diabetes** cannot control the amount of a sugar called **glucose** in their blood. The amount of glucose in the blood increases after a meal, but if it gets too high it can damage the kidneys and the brain. People with the disease inject a chemical called **insulin** which lowers the amount of glucose in the blood. Many diabetics also avoid eating too many sugary things to stop the glucose level getting too high.

A diabetic injecting insulin.

1 The bodies of people with diabetes cannot make a certain chemical.
a) What do you think this chemical is called?
b) What does this chemical do?

People who have **coeliac disease** (pronounced *see-li-ack*) avoid eating wheat products. They are allergic to a protein in wheat called gluten. The gluten causes parts of the intestine to become damaged and stops nutrients getting from their food into their bodies.

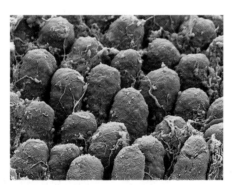

A normal intestine.

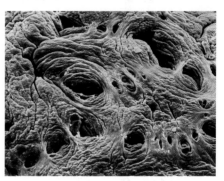

An intestine damaged by coeliac disease.

2 Young children with coeliac disease may not grow very well. Why do you think this is?

3 Name two foods that someone with coeliac disease would not eat.

When you eat proteins your body breaks them up into **amino acids**. Your liver gets rid of any extra amino acids that your body does not need. However, in a disease called **phenylketonuria** (PKU), one amino acid (phenylalanine) cannot be got rid of. It builds up in the body and causes brain problems. People with this disease avoid eating foods which contain proteins that have a lot of phenylalanine in them.

4 a) What is phenylalanine?
b) Why do people with phenylketonuria avoid foods with proteins containing phenylalanine?

5 a) Find out what gout is.
b) Find out what foods people with gout should avoid.

What do the parts of the digestive system do?

The food that you eat needs to be turned into a form that your body can use. This process is called **digestion**. It happens as your food passes down a tube made up of different organs, called the **gut**, which runs from your mouth to your **anus**. Other organs (like the liver) also help with digestion. The gut and the other organs make up the **digestive system**.

1 What process turns our food into a form that we can use?

2 What is the gut?

Putting food in your mouth is called **feeding** or **ingestion**. Teeth grind the food into smaller pieces. The main grinding teeth (**molars**) are at the back of the mouth. The **salivary glands** produce a liquid called **saliva**. Saliva helps make the food moist so that it is easy to swallow.

salivary gland

When you swallow, the windpipe is shut off and food goes into the **gullet** (or food pipe). Muscles in the wall of the gullet make the tube above the food narrower. They **contract**. Food is moved through the rest of the digestive system in the same way.

The particles that make up food are called molecules. Small molecules are taken into the body (**absorbed**) through the wall of the **small intestine**.

In the **stomach** the food is churned up with strong acid (pH 1–2).

Food that we cannot digest (**fibre**) goes into the **large intestine**, where water is removed. This forms a more solid material called **faeces** (pronounced '*fee-sees*').

*The **appendix** is a small tube. In some animals it helps to digest grass. In humans it has no real job and sometimes gets infected. This is called appendicitis. If this happens the appendix is usually removed.*

Faeces are stored in the **rectum**. They are eventually pushed out of the **anus**. They are eliminated or **egested**.

3 a) Where is saliva produced?
    b) What does it do?

The digestive system.

The gut is about 8 m long. The long intestines are coiled up so that they can fit inside the body. It normally takes between 24 and 48 hours for food to go through the gut. Fibre in your diet helps this to happen.

The photographs show models of some molecules found in your food. Only molecules of the same size or smaller than glucose can be absorbed by the small intestine.

4 What is the job of the large intestine?

5 a) Write down a list of the organs in the gut.
 b) How is food moved through the gut?
 c) How long does this take?
 d) Name one other organ, not in the gut, that is part of the digestive system.

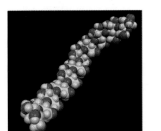
A starch molecule (a carbohydrate).

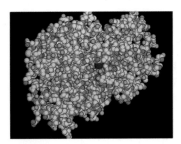
A protein molecule.

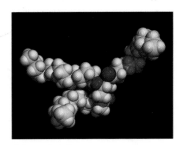
A fat molecule.

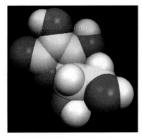
A vitamin C molecule.

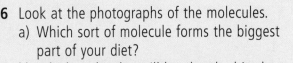
6 Look at the photographs of the molecules.
 a) Which sort of molecule forms the biggest part of your diet?
 b) Which molecules will be absorbed in the small intestine?
 c) From your answer to part b) suggest which molecule will be the most easily absorbed.
 d) The molecules that cannot be absorbed are still important for the body. What do you think has to happen to them so they can be absorbed?

A glucose molecule (a type of carbohydrate called a sugar).

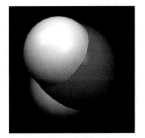
A water molecule.

Most of the food we eat is **insoluble**. To make use of our food, most of it needs to be broken apart into smaller, soluble substances. This is what happens in digestion. Special chemicals called **enzymes** do this.

Sugars (e.g. glucose), vitamins and minerals are small and soluble in water and so can pass through the wall of the small intestine. Larger insoluble molecules, like starch, fats and proteins need to be broken up into small, soluble molecules by enzymes.

7 a) Where are food substances absorbed?
 b) How do enzymes help your food to be absorbed?

8 a) Name one soluble carbohydrate.
 b) Name one insoluble carbohydrate.

You should know...
- **What the digestive system is and what it does.**
- **Why enzymes are needed to break apart larger molecules.**

How is our food digested?

Many parts of the digestive system produce **digestive juices** which contain enzymes. Enzymes digest large molecules into small, soluble ones. The small, soluble molecules get through the wall of the small intestine and into the blood. We say that the molecules are **absorbed** by the small intestine.

The diagram shows a model gut. Visking tubing is a very thin material containing microscopic holes which only small, soluble molecules can pass through. The inside of the tubing represents the inside of the small intestine. The water around the outside of the tubing represents the blood in the body.

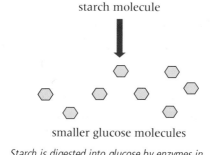
enzymes

starch molecule

smaller glucose molecules

Starch is digested into glucose by enzymes in digestive juices.

The model gut only works well if the temperature is about 37 °C. This is because enzymes have a certain temperature that they work best at. The enzymes in humans work best at body temperature (37 °C).

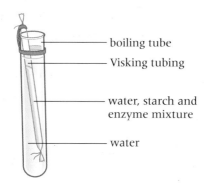
boiling tube

Visking tubing

water, starch and enzyme mixture

water

> **1** a) Which food substance is inside the tubing?
> b) Which substance would you expect to find in the water after 10 minutes?
> c) Draw a series of diagrams to show what happens in the model gut over 30 minutes. Label your drawings to explain what happens.

P An enzyme found in the small intestine is called **amylase**. It breaks down starch. How would you investigate which factors affect how quickly amylase works?

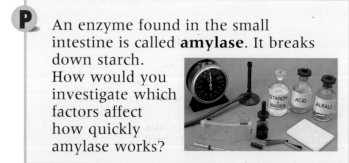

There are enzymes in saliva which break down starch. They only work properly at about pH7 which is the pH in the mouth. They stop working when the food reaches the stomach because the stomach contains hydrochloric acid. The stomach contains enzymes which break down proteins.

You should know...

- **Each enzyme works best at a particular temperature and pH.**

- **Small molecules are absorbed into the blood by the small intestine.**

> **2** Suggest a pH at which the enzymes in the stomach work best.
>
> **3** The small intestine produces an enzyme called protease.
> a) What temperature do you think protease works best at?
> b) What food substance do you think protease breaks up? Choose from this list:
>   fats   starch   proteins   minerals   salts   vitamins   fibre
>
> **4** How do small molecules get into the blood?

How do the liver and pancreas help with digestion?

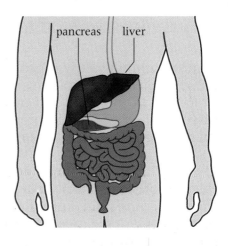

The liver and the pancreas are organs that help with digestion.

The **liver** makes a green substance called **bile**, which is released into the small intestine. Bile does not contain enzymes. It is an alkali and cancels out (**neutralises**) the stomach acid. Bile splits fat into small droplets forming an **emulsion** (a liquid mixed in with another liquid). These small droplets of fat give the enzymes more area to work on and so the fat is digested quicker.

The beakers contain cooking oil (a fat) and water. The beaker on the left has had bile salts added. This has formed an emulsion.

1 a) What is an emulsion?
  b) What forms the emulsion in the small intestine?
  c) Explain how an emulsion helps digestion.

The small intestine makes some enzymes. Others are added by the **pancreas**. Each enzyme only breaks down one sort of molecule. **Amylase** breaks down starch, forming smaller molecules of a sugar called **maltose**. Maltose is still quite big and so another enzyme, called **maltase**, cuts it up into another sugar called **glucose**. Other enzymes digest the other substances in our food.

There are different kinds of amino acids. Some are **essential amino acids** – we must eat proteins containing these to stay healthy. Different proteins contain different amino acids and so we need to eat proteins from different foods to make sure we get all the amino acids we need.

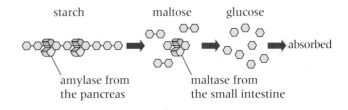

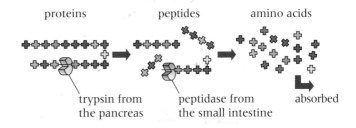

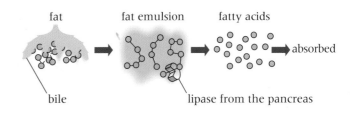

2 a) What is an essential amino acid?
  b) Try to find out the name of one of these.

3 A sugar called sucrose is found in our food. Suggest a name for the enzyme that breaks up sucrose.

4 Amylase is found in saliva. Why do you think that it needs to be added again by the pancreas?

Why is digested food transported around the body?

Digestion breaks down insoluble substances into smaller, soluble ones. Only soluble molecules can go through the wall of the small intestine and into the **blood**. They are said to be **absorbed** by the small intestine. The wall of the small intestine is very thin so that substances are absorbed quickly.

The small intestine is lined with **villi**. These look like fingers (one finger is called a villus). They give a large surface area. The larger the surface area, the faster the substances can be absorbed.

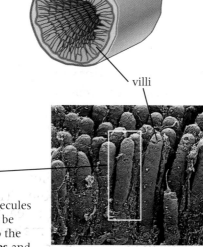

small intestine

villi

1 a) We say that digested food is absorbed. What does this mean?
 b) Where does this happen?

Large, insoluble molecules cannot be absorbed.

The small, soluble molecules made by digestion can be absorbed. They go into the blood in the **capillaries** and then into a **vein**.

vein

artery

A villus.

Due to the villi, the total surface area of the small intestine is 10 m^2.

P Bath towels have things like villi on them, bed sheets do not. How would you investigate which material absorbs water more quickly?

Digested food passes into **capillaries** in the middle of the villi. Capillaries are tiny tubes that carry blood. The digested food dissolves in the blood and is carried around the body.

2 How is dissolved food carried around the body?

3 a) Where in your body are villi found?
 b) Make a labelled drawing of a villus to explain what it does.

The tubes that carry the blood around the body are called **blood vessels** and the smallest of these are capillaries. Blood is pumped by the **heart**. **Arteries** are blood vessels coming from the heart. **Veins** are blood vessels going to the heart.

Capillaries often link arteries with veins and can pick up substances (in the small intestine, for example) or drop them off.

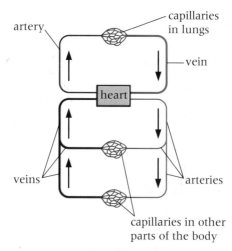

artery

capillaries in lungs

vein

heart

veins

arteries

capillaries in other parts of the body

The heart and blood vessels form the
circulatory system.

4 Write down one difference between arteries and veins.

5 What do you think capillaries in the lungs pick up?

6 How does a cell in the liver get a supply of digested food?

All the cells in our bodies need digested food. They use it to release energy using **respiration** and to make new substances.

Tissues in the body contain many capillaries so that the cells are never far from a source of digested food. The liquid part of the blood can leak out of capillaries and form **tissue fluid**. This carries dissolved digested food molecules to the cells.

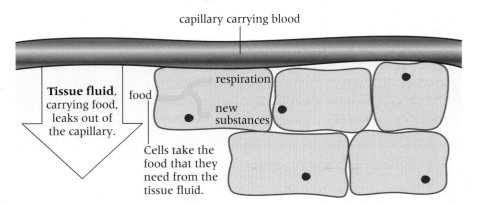

capillary carrying blood

Tissue fluid, carrying food, leaks out of the capillary.

food

respiration

new substances

Cells take the food that they need from the tissue fluid.

Some of the energy released by respiration is heat energy. This can help us to stay warm. Some of the energy is used to work muscles so that we can move.

Many thousands of chemical reactions occur in our bodies. These reactions need energy to make them happen. Many of the reactions produce new substances for the body to use. The raw materials for these new substances come from our food. The new substances are used to make new cells. New cells help us to grow and repair our bodies.

7 Different foods contain different amounts of chemical energy. Fast running uses up about 44 kJ each minute.
   a) Look at the nutrition information label. If you were running fast, how many minutes worth of energy would 200 g of this food give you?
   b) Which part of this food gives the most energy?
   c) Not all the energy from the food is used to help you run. What else is it used for?

8 Look again at the nutrition label below.
   a) How much energy is there in 100 g of the food shown?
   b) One of the contents gives no energy at all. Which one?
   c) Why is this?
   d) What happens to this material?

9 Make a list of three things that the body uses energy for.

NUTRITION INFORMATION

Typical Values	Amount per 100 g	Amount per Serving (200 g)
Energy	264 kJ	527 kJ
Protein	2.0 g	4.1 g
Carbohydrate (of which sugars)	12.6 g (4.4 g)	25.2 g (8.8 g)
Fat (of which saturates)	0.4 g (0.2 g)	0.8 g (0.4 g)
Fibre	0.6 g	1.2 g

You should know...

- Dissolved food can pass into blood capillaries from the small intestine.
- Digested food is dissolved in blood and carried around the body in the circulatory system.
- Digested food is used for respiration and to make new substances.

How is digested food used?

All the cells in our bodies need digested food. They use it for growth, to make new substances and to release energy using **respiration**. Some of the energy released by respiration is heat energy which helps to keep us warm.

One of the small molecules produced by digestion is called **glucose**. It is a very important molecule that provides us with energy. Many people drink 'high energy drinks' when they exercise. These contain glucose.

In the London Marathon there are regular places where people can pick up a 'high energy drink'.

1   What do cells use digested food for?

2   Why do you think people running marathons take 'high energy drinks' rather than eat a food containing carbohydrates? (*Hint*: Think about how long digestion takes.)

Glucose is carried around the body dissolved in the blood, like many of the substances produced by digestion. The blood takes it to all the cells where it is needed. The cells use up the glucose in respiration which releases energy. All living cells respire and so they all need a supply of glucose.

3   What does respiration release?

4   a) In a marathon runner, which cell will need the most glucose? Choose from one of these:
      nerve cell in the brain   skin cell on the arm
      muscle cell in the leg
    b) Explain your answer using the word 'respiration'.

The 'marathon' takes its name from the battle of Marathon in 490 BC between the Greeks and Persians. The Greeks won the battle and appointed a runner called Phidippides to run to Athens with the news, a distance of about 40 km (25 miles). However, Phidippides had already run about 450 km in the previous week. After he delivered his message in Athens, he died. The modern marathon is 26.2 miles, which was set for the 1908 Olympic Games in London. It was the distance between Windsor Castle and King Edward VII's royal box in White City Stadium!

Respiration versus burning

Burning is a chemical reaction that releases energy. Sugar can be made to burn. The sugar is used up, along with oxygen from the air. Carbon dioxide and water are made.

Respiration is a bit like burning. It also releases energy, needs oxygen and produces carbon dioxide and water. Although some of the energy is released as heat, cells don't catch fire!

This sugar is burning. Energy is being released.

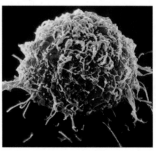

This cell is respiring. Energy is being released.

Respiration is a series of carefully controlled chemical reactions. We can sum up these reactions in a **word equation**:

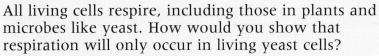

oxygen + glucose ⟶ carbon dioxide + water (+ energy)

reactants   products

'Energy' is in brackets because it is not a substance. This kind of respiration is called **aerobic respiration** because it needs oxygen from the air.

P

All living cells respire, including those in plants and microbes like yeast. How would you show that respiration will only occur in living yeast cells?
- What would you test for?
- How would you do your test or tests?

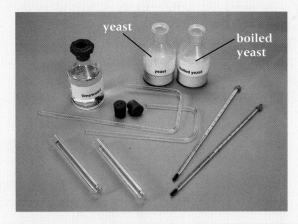

yeast   boiled yeast

Robert Boyle (1627–1691) discovered that removing all the air from a glass jar put out a candle and killed small animals inside the jar. This showed that respiration and burning both need oxygen from the air.

---

5 Why is the respiration in cells called 'aerobic' respiration?

6 How is glucose carried to the cells?

---

7 a) Write out the word equation for aerobic respiration.
   b) Write out the word equation for burning glucose.
   c) List four ways in which aerobic respiration is like burning.
   d) List one way in which they are different.
   e) Name two sorts of energy released by burning.

8 Look at the picture. Beaker X contains peas that are starting to grow. Beaker Y contains boiled peas.
   a) In which beaker will the temperature rise?
   b) In which beaker will carbon dioxide be made?
   c) Explain your answers.

X   Y

You should know...

- **Digested food is needed for growth, making new substances and respiration.**
- **Glucose is used by living cells to release energy in respiration.**
- **The word equation for aerobic respiration.**

How does the circulatory system carry substances around the body?

Oxygen and digested food travel around the body in the blood. Blood flows through tubes called **blood vessels**. The smallest blood vessels are **capillaries**. They have thin walls with tiny gaps in so that small molecules, like water, can easily get into and out of them.

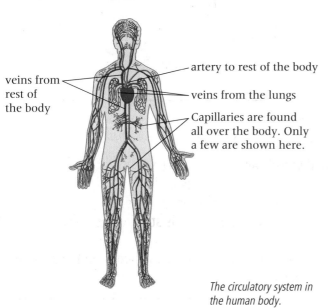

veins from rest of the body

artery to rest of the body

veins from the lungs

Capillaries are found all over the body. Only a few are shown here.

The circulatory system in the human body.

1 a) What are capillaries?
  b) Why can substances get into and out of capillaries easily?

When glucose is **absorbed** by the small intestine it goes into capillaries in the wall of the small intestine. Oxygen goes into capillaries that are inside the walls of the lungs.

Blood is pumped through the capillaries and all the other blood vessels by the **heart**. There are two other sorts of blood vessel: **arteries** and **veins**. Arteries are blood vessels carrying blood away from the heart and veins are blood vessels carrying blood towards the heart. The heart and blood vessels make up the **circulatory system**.

2 What are the parts of the circulatory system?

3 Write down one difference between arteries and veins.

The right-hand side of your heart receives blood from all over the body. This side of the heart pumps the blood to the lungs where oxygen enters it. The left-hand side of your heart receives blood from the lungs and pumps it around the rest of the body. This side of the heart is bigger because it has to pump harder to get the blood all the way around the body.

There are many branches in the circulatory system. Only a few are shown here.

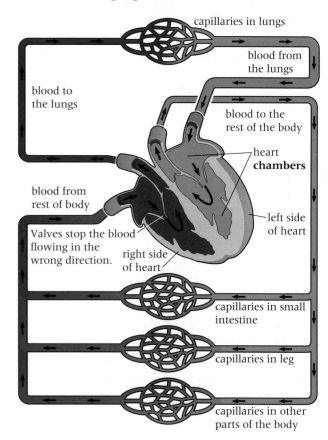

capillaries in lungs

blood from the lungs

blood to the lungs

blood to the rest of the body

heart **chambers**

blood from rest of body

left side of heart

Valves stop the blood flowing in the wrong direction.

right side of heart

capillaries in small intestine

capillaries in leg

capillaries in other parts of the body

4 a) Draw a flow chart to show the route a glucose molecule would take from the small intestine to a leg muscle cell. Start it like this:

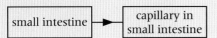

b) Draw a similar chart to show the route an oxygen molecule would take from the lungs to a leg muscle cell.

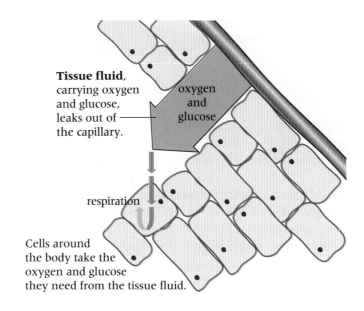

Tissue fluid, carrying oxygen and glucose, leaks out of the capillary.

oxygen and glucose

respiration

Cells around the body take the oxygen and glucose they need from the tissue fluid.

Oxygen is carried by **red blood cells**. Glucose is dissolved in the liquid part of the blood (called **plasma**). Plasma leaks out of the capillaries and forms **tissue fluid** around cells in the body. Some of the oxygen leaves the red blood cells and dissolves in the tissue fluid. The red blood cells stay inside the capillary.

5 a) What is tissue fluid?
b) What does tissue fluid contain?

6 a) Which blood vessels allow substances to be exchanged between the blood and other cells in the body?
b) What liquid comes out of these blood vessels?
c) Why do you think the red blood cells stay in these blood vessels?
d) This process is similar to a laboratory method used to separate things. Which method?

If you press two fingers firmly onto your wrist, you can feel your blood being pumped. This is called your **pulse**. Your **pulse rate** is the number of beats you can feel in one minute.

In an average lifetime the heart beats 4 000 000 000 times without stopping.

P How would you find out what effect exercise has on your pulse rate?

7 What is a pulse rate?

8 a) Which side of the heart is bigger?
b) Why is this?
c) What do the heart valves do?

You should know...

● **Blood carries oxygen and glucose around the body in the circulatory system.**

How have ideas about circulation changed?

Galen was a Greek physician (doctor) who cut up dead animals to see what they were like inside. He assumed that humans were like animals inside.

Galen also believed that blood passed from one side of the heart to the other through invisible holes. He believed this because he could see small pits in the wall separating the two sides of the heart which he thought had holes in the end. He also found that unborn mammals had large holes in their hearts. We now know that these holes close up at birth. Galen thought that veins and arteries formed two separate systems and that blood flowed backwards and forwards in these vessels.

Galen (c.130–c.201).

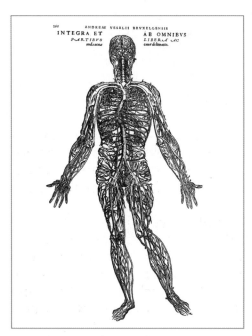

Andreas Vesalius (1514–1564) was a Belgian doctor who cut up many human bodies. However, the Church did not allow this and so he resorted to grave digging! Vesalius showed that many of Galen's drawings of the insides of humans were in fact drawings of the insides of animals. Although Vesalius still believed that blood flowed backwards and forwards in the blood vessels, he showed that there were no small holes in the heart. At first people refused to believe that Galen was wrong, but eventually other scientists discovered more evidence proving that Vesalius was right.

The idea of the circulatory system that we believe today was first suggested by William Harvey (1578–1657). Part of his evidence came from observing that living hearts take in and pump out blood when they beat.

A page from Vesalius' book which showed the first detailed drawings of the inside of the human body.

---

1 a) What arguments did Galen use to support his theory that blood flowed through the wall in the middle of the heart?

b) Suggest a simple experiment that Vesalius might have done to provide evidence that Galen was wrong.

2 Why do you think it took hundreds of years before progress was made in the understanding of the circulatory system?

3 Why was Vesalius' method of working out how the human body worked better than Galen's?

4 Many other scientists have made discoveries about the heart and the circulatory system. Find out about what one or more of these scientists discovered and the evidence they used: Ibn al-Nafis (1213–1288), Girolamo Fabrizio (c.1533–1619), William Withering (1741–1799).

8Bc Aerobics

What are the effects of getting too little oxygen?

The word **aerobic** means 'with air'. Aerobic respiration is respiration that needs air to provide a source of oxygen. Aerobics is a type of exercise that is slow enough to allow you to breathe easily. This means you can get enough oxygen for all your cells to use aerobic respiration and release lots of energy. Walking and jogging are aerobic exercises, which is why you can continue doing them for long periods of time.

Some exercise is very hard and you cannot do it for long because more oxygen is needed than your lungs can take out of the air.

> **?** 1 a) What are aerobic exercises?
>   b) Give three examples of aerobic exercise.
>
>   2 Describe two effects on your body when you do very hard exercise.

> **P** The number of times you breathe in and out in a minute is called your **breathing rate**. How would you find out how light and hard exercise affect your breathing rate?

 In cold conditions the blood vessels in your skin become narrow and less blood reaches the cells. If this happens for a long time in very cold temperatures the cells die. This is called frostbite. Many mountaineers have lost fingers and toes due to frostbite.

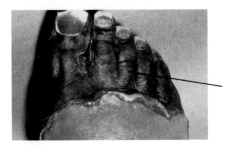

— frostbite

In a disease called emphysema, the lungs cannot take very much oxygen out of the air. Patients suffer from shortness of breath even when resting and they often feel very tired.

In other diseases blood vessels can get blocked up. This stops some tissues getting the oxygen and glucose that they need and the cells may die. In **heart disease** the blood vessels supplying the muscles of the heart get blocked and this can lead to a **heart attack**.

> **?** 3 There is less air high up a mountain. Describe how a mountaineer might feel when high up a mountain.
>
>   4 Explain how a heart attack is caused.

> **You should know...**
> ● Some of the effects of too little oxygen.

What happens to the products of respiration?

The **reactants** for respiration are glucose and oxygen. They are carried around the body in the blood. Some of the blood plasma leaks out of the capillaries. This forms **tissue fluid** which contains glucose and oxygen and bathes the cells. Respiring cells absorb the chemicals they need from this fluid.

oxygen + glucose ⟶ carbon dioxide + water (+ energy)

reactants   products

Aerobic respiration.

Respiration occurs in the cytoplasm of cells. Energy is released and the waste products carbon dioxide and water are made. Carbon dioxide is poisonous in large amounts, and so it has to be removed quickly. It dissolves in the tissue fluid and goes back into the blood plasma. The blood carries it to the lungs where it is got rid of (**excreted**).

? 1 What are the reactants in aerobic respiration?

2 What are the products of aerobic respiration?

3 Why must all cells respire?

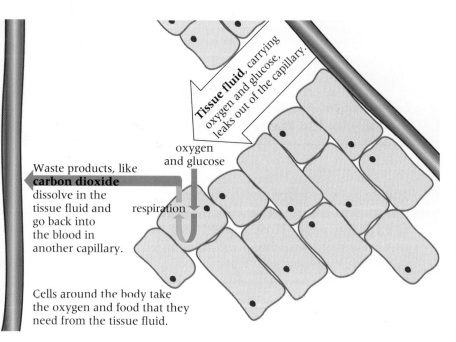

Tissue fluid, carrying oxygen and glucose, leaks out of the capillary.

oxygen and glucose

Waste products, like **carbon dioxide** dissolve in the tissue fluid and go back into the blood in another capillary.

respiration

Cells around the body take the oxygen and food that they need from the tissue fluid.

? 4 Name two substances that are exchanged between tissue fluid and cells.

5 How is carbon dioxide carried in the blood?

You should know...

● **How the reactants and products of respiration are exchanged between cells and tissue fluid.**

! *Cyanide is a poisonous substance. It causes death very quickly by stopping aerobic respiration. Cells cannot survive without energy.*

During World War II, a type of cyanide (Zyklon B) was used in gas chambers by the Nazis. Today, some parts of the USA still use cyanide to kill people convicted of serious offences.

A gas chamber in a US prison.

Anaerobic respiration

What happens when the body is short of oxygen?

During exercise, your breathing rate increases to take in more oxygen and to excrete the toxic carbon dioxide, produced in the cells, as quickly as possible. Your heart rate increases to supply glucose and oxygen to the muscle cells and to remove the carbon dioxide rapidly.

Despite these changes, sometimes the body cannot provide the muscles with enough oxygen. The cells need more energy so they start to respire **anaerobically**. This means that they break down glucose without oxygen to release energy.

glucose ⟶ lactic acid (+ a little energy)

Anaerobic respiration.

Anaerobic respiration does not release as much energy as aerobic respiration because not all of the energy is released from each glucose molecule. The lactic acid that is produced still has quite a bit of energy locked up in it. Muscles cannot respire anaerobically for long because lactic acid is poisonous. If too much builds up in the muscle cells, it causes cramp.

When you stop exercising you continue to pant in order to supply oxygen for aerobic respiration to break down the lactic acid. The amount of oxygen required to do this is called the **oxygen debt**.

At the end of hard exercise, people pant for a little while and sometimes get cramp in their muscles.

 When people hold their breath, the oxygen in their bodies starts to run out and some cells will start to respire anaerobically. On 3 July 2001, Martin Stepanek held his breath underwater for 8 minutes 6 seconds.

Deborah Andollo, from Cuba, taking part in an underwater holding breath contest.

1 a) What changes happen to the body during exercise?
   b) Why do these changes happen?

2 What do you think is meant by the term 'anaerobic'?

3 Give two differences between aerobic and anaerobic respiration.

4 Why is less energy released in anaerobic respiration?

5 What causes cramp?

6 Why do you pant when you stop exercising?

7 What is meant by the term 'oxygen debt'?

How are gases exchanged in the lungs?

Aerobic respiration uses glucose and oxygen which are carried around your body in your **blood**. The **digestive system** gets glucose into the blood. The **breathing system** (or **respiratory system**) gets oxygen into your blood and removes (excretes) carbon dioxide from it.

Breathing is when muscles change the size of your lungs. When you breathe in (**inhale**), the muscles make your lungs get bigger. When you breathe out (**exhale**), the muscles make your lungs smaller. The movement of air into and out of your lungs is called **ventilation**.

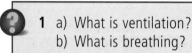

1 a) What is ventilation?
b) What is breathing?

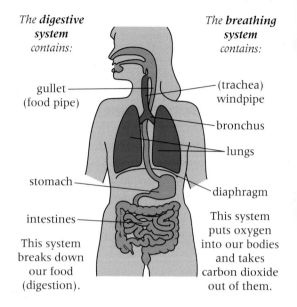

The **digestive system** contains:
- gullet (food pipe)
- stomach
- intestines

This system breaks down our food (digestion).

The **breathing system** contains:
- (trachea) windpipe
- bronchus
- lungs
- diaphragm

This system puts oxygen into our bodies and takes carbon dioxide out of them.

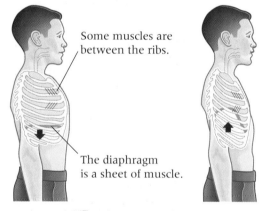

Some muscles are between the ribs.

The diaphragm is a sheet of muscle.

Breathing in (inhalation).   *Breathing out (exhalation).*

The lungs contain thousands of small **air sacs** containing tiny pockets called **alveoli**. These give the lungs a large surface area for absorbing oxygen and excreting carbon dioxide. They have thin walls (only one cell thick) so that gases diffuse easily across them. **Diffusion** is when particles move from a place where there are a lot of them to a place where there are less of them. Oxygen diffuses into the blood and carbon dioxide diffuses out of the blood. The alveoli are surrounded by many blood capillaries, which also have thin walls so substances can easily pass into and out of the blood. When oxygen is being carried by the **red blood cells**, it makes them look redder.

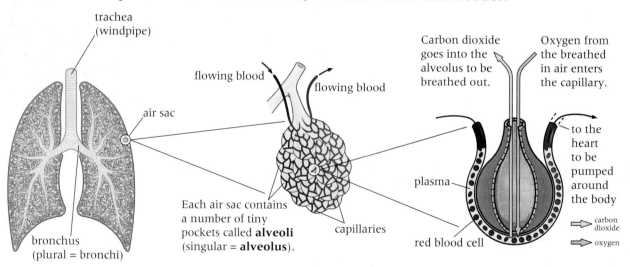

trachea (windpipe)

air sac

bronchus (plural = bronchi)

flowing blood

flowing blood

Each air sac contains a number of tiny pockets called **alveoli** (singular = **alveolus**).

capillaries

Carbon dioxide goes into the alveolus to be breathed out.

Oxygen from the breathed in air enters the capillary.

to the heart to be pumped around the body

plasma

red blood cell

carbon dioxide

oxygen

Lungs.   *An air sac.*   *An alveolus.*

Picking up oxygen and getting rid of carbon dioxide in the alveoli is called **gas exchange**.

 The surface area of the lungs is enormous. If you flattened out all the alveoli they would cover a tennis court!

2 What is diffusion?

3 What are capillaries?

4 What is gas exchange?

5 Where in the lungs does gas exchange occur?

6 List three ways in which the lungs are adapted for gas exchange.

7 a) The lungs are said to excrete a substance. What does excrete mean?
  b) What is the substance that they excrete?

8 How are each of these substances carried by the blood?
  a) oxygen   b) carbon dioxide

A sticky liquid called **mucus** is produced by cells in the tubes leading into the lungs. This traps dirt and germs. Tiny hairs, called **cilia**, are found on **ciliated epithelial cells** in the **trachea** and **bronchi**. These hairs sweep the mucus out of the lungs and into the gullet where it is swallowed. This is how the lungs are kept clean. Chemicals in cigarette smoke stop cilia working and so smokers are more likely to get lung infections.

Sometimes the lungs get damaged. For example, in a disease called emphysema, the lungs develop large holes, which can fill up with liquid. Inhaled dust can also cause tears in the delicate lung tissue.

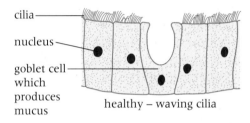
healthy – waving cilia

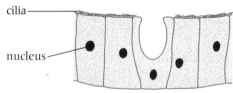
unhealthy – 'lifeless' cilia

Healthy lungs.

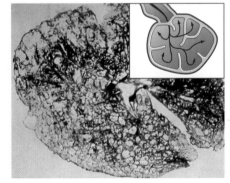
Emphysema.

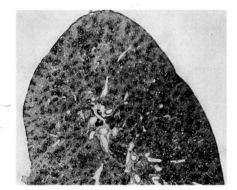
Dust damage.

9 Look at the pictures showing lung damage.
  a) Describe the differences between a healthy lung and one from someone with emphysema.
  b) Explain how damage to the lung might affect gas exchange.

You should know...
- **How the lungs carry out gas exchange.**
- **How lung damage can affect gas exchange.**

How are inhaled and exhaled air different?

The air we breathe in is called **inhaled air**. This is the normal air around us. The air we breathe out is called **exhaled air**.

exhaled air   normal air

>
> **1** Look at the picture of the two gas jars.
>   a) In which gas jar do you think the candle will burn for the longest time?
>   b) Explain your answer.

The table shows the differences between inhaled and exhaled air. Some of these differences are due to respiration, which happens in all your cells.

	Inhaled air	Exhaled air
Nitrogen gas	78%	78%
Oxygen gas	21%	16%
Carbon dioxide gas	0.03%	4%
Water vapour	variable	more
Temperature	variable	warmer
Dirt particles	variable	cleaner

Differences between inhaled and exhaled air.

 P How could you show that exhaled air contains more carbon dioxide and water, and is warmer than inhaled air?

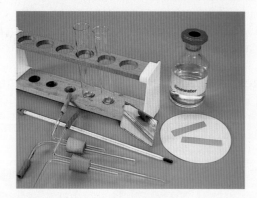

>
> **2** The amount of nitrogen in inhaled air is the same as that in exhaled air. Suggest a reason for this.
>
> **3** Why is there less oxygen in exhaled air than inhaled air?
>
> **4** Why is there more carbon dioxide in exhaled air than inhaled air?
>
> **5** Exhaled air is warmer than inhaled air. Explain why.
>
> **6** Inhaled air is dirtier than exhaled air. Explain why.
>
> **7** Display the information comparing inhaled and exhaled air as two pie charts.

Organisms that live in water also need oxygen for respiration. The gas is dissolved in the water.

Plants that grow underwater get their oxygen by diffusion. Oxygen diffuses into the cells from the surrounding water.

A fish gets oxygen by taking in water through its mouth and forcing it over the **gills**. The gills have a large surface area and a good blood supply so that oxygen can quickly diffuse from the water into the blood.

If warm water is released into rivers from power stations, it reduces the amount of oxygen dissolved in the water. In some cases the fish can die.

Oxygen diffuses into the leaves from the water.

8 Explain how fish get their oxygen from the water.

9 Gills are adapted to absorb lots of oxygen. Explain how.

10 How do you think fish excrete carbon dioxide?

11 What happens if warm water is released into rivers?

12 a) What colour would hydrogencarbonate indicator solution turn if you breathed into it through a straw?
   b) Explain why it would turn this colour.

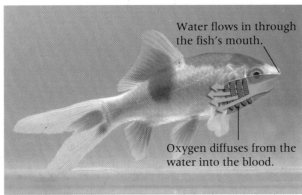
Water flows in through the fish's mouth.

Oxygen diffuses from the water into the blood.

How a fish carries out gas exchange.

P

Hydrogencarbonate indicator changes colour depending on how much carbon dioxide is dissolved in it.
How could you show that other plants and animals produce carbon dioxide when they respire?
• You could also try to find out what affects the amount of carbon dioxide produced.

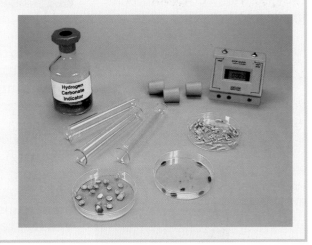

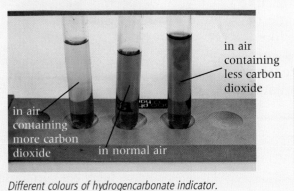

in air containing less carbon dioxide

in air containing more carbon dioxide

in normal air

Different colours of hydrogencarbonate indicator.

You should know...
● **The differences between inhaled and exhaled air.**
● **Respiration occurs in all organisms.**

What are microbes?

Living things are called **organisms**. Some organisms are very small (often made of only one cell) and we need microscopes to see them. Organisms like this are called **micro-organisms**, or **microbes** for short.

The seven life processes
Movement (move all or parts of themselves)
Reproduction (make more living things like themselves)
Sensitivity (sense and react to things around them)
Growth (increase in cell size and/or number)
Respiration (use a chemical reaction to release energy from food)
Excretion (get rid of waste materials that they make)
Nutrition (need various substances to help them respire and grow)

All organisms must do all these things.

 1 How many cells do many micro-organisms have?

Viruses are the smallest type of microbe. They are very difficult to see even with the most powerful microscope. The largest ones are only about 0.000 000 3 mm big! Many scientists do not think that they are organisms at all because they cannot live without being inside another cell.

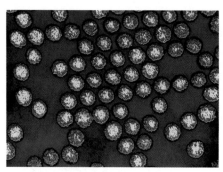
Viruses at a magnification of ×220 000.

2 Why are viruses so difficult to see?

3 List two things that organisms do which viruses do not do for themselves.

A bacterium at a magnification of ×90 000.

Bacteria are much bigger than viruses and are definitely living things. The singular of bacteria is **bacterium**.

Another group of organisms are **fungi** (the singular is **fungus**). Some fungi, like mushrooms, are made of many cells. Others, like **yeast**, are microbes and made of one cell. Yeast are usually bigger than bacteria.

Yeast cells at a magnification of ×1380.

 When yeast respire they use up a sugar (like glucose) and produce carbon dioxide. How might you find out the best conditions for yeast to respire?

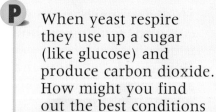

water   glucose   yeast culture

4 Name one sort of fungus that is a microbe.

5 Make a table to compare the three different sorts of microbes.

You should know...
- **Viruses, bacteria and some fungi are microbes.**

Microbe structure

What are the major differences between microbes?

Organisms can be **classified** into one of five **kingdoms** by what their cells look like.

1 Which kingdoms contain organisms that can make their own food?

	Kingdom				
Cell part	Bacteria	Protoctists	Fungi	Plants	Animals
Nucleus	Absent	Present	Present	Present	Present
Cell wall	Soft cell wall made of glycoprotein	Different types in different species	Mainly made of chitin	Mainly made of cellulose	Absent
Chloroplasts	Absent	Found in some species	Absent	Present	Absent

Viruses are not really living and so do not have a kingdom. They are made of a **protein coat** which contains a **strand of genes**. The genes contain the instructions for making new viruses. When a virus gets into a cell, the virus genes cause the cell to make new copies of the virus. This is known as **replication**.

Bacteria are single cells which do not contain a nucleus. Their genes are found on a circular **chromosome**. On the outside of a bacterium is a soft cell wall. Some bacteria have 'tails' (called **flagellae**) which help them move.

protein coat

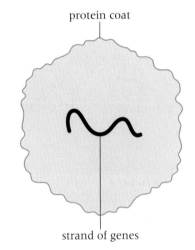

strand of genes

A virus is very simple.

2 What is a virus made up of?

3 a) What is virus replication?
   b) Why do you think it is not called 'reproduction'?

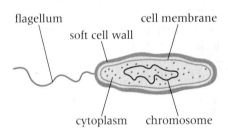

flagellum   cell membrane
soft cell wall
cytoplasm   chromosome

Bacteria are living cells.

4 a) List one thing that an animal cell has but a bacterium cell does not.
   b) List two things that both animal cells and bacterium cells have.

Like all fungi, yeast have a nucleus which contains chromosomes. They also have vacuoles to store substances in.

food storage granules

nucleus

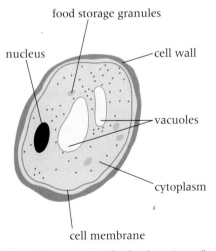

cell wall

vacuoles

cytoplasm

cell membrane

Yeast cells are more complex than bacterium cells.

5 List two differences between bacterium cells and yeast cells.

6 Algae (singular = alga) are a type of protoctist. Find and draw a diagram showing an alga cell. Label your drawing and write down the name of the alga. Write down where you found out the information.

29

How are microbes used?

Many microbes are useful. Some bacteria and fungi are used to make foods and drinks.

Some types of yeast are very important and are used in baking and brewing.

made with the help of fungi | made with the help of bacteria | made with the help of fungi and bacteria

? **1** List three foods or drinks that are made with the help of yeast.

Baking

Bread dough contains flour, water, sugar and yeast. The sugar allows the yeast to grow, respire and reproduce.

The dough is stretched and folded (kneaded) to trap air in it so that the yeast have enough oxygen for **aerobic respiration**.

? **2** Why is bread kneaded?

3 What is the word equation for aerobic respiration?

glucose + oxygen ⟶ carbon dioxide + water (+ energy)
(a sugar)

Aerobic respiration.

Aerobic respiration produces carbon dioxide. The bubbles of this gas make the dough rise.

The dough is then baked in an oven.

P How could you find out the best conditions for getting bread to rise the furthest?

water

Brewing

Beer and wine are also made using yeast. However, this time the aim is to keep air out of the mixture. If there is no oxygen, yeast use **anaerobic respiration** instead, which produces **ethanol** (alcohol). When yeast respire anaerobically it is known as **fermentation**. If the yeast respire on sugars found in barley grains, beer is made. Grapes are used to make wine.

 Usually when making wine, the carbon dioxide escapes. When champagne is made, the carbon dioxide is kept in the wine to give it its fizz.

glucose ⟶ carbon dioxide + ethanol (+ energy)
(a sugar)

4 a) What is anaerobic respiration?
b) What is it called when yeast respire anaerobically?

Yeast reproduce by **budding**. A new cell grows out of a 'parent' cell. The new cell grows and then it too can produce a 'bud cell'.

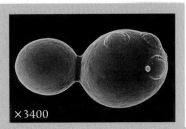
×3400

Given the right conditions (warmth, moisture and plenty of sugar), microbes like yeast will grow and reproduce very quickly. Starting off with a few yeast cells, you can soon end up with many millions. However, the **population** of yeast cells will not keep growing forever. Eventually the sugar will run out and the population will stop growing. Something that slows down or stops a population growing is known as a **limiting factor**.

Only a few yeast cells and so the population increases slowly.

Many more yeast cells and so the population grows very quickly.

As the glucose starts to run out (becomes a limiting factor) the growth of the population slows down, and the population soon stops growing.

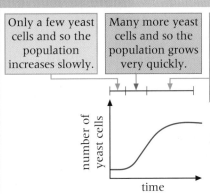

5 What is a 'population'?

6 Some yeast cells are added to a beaker of glucose solution. The number of yeast cells is found to increase for eight hours and then it stops increasing.
a) Why did the number of cells increase?
b) Why did the number of cells stop increasing?

7 Some bread dough is made so that it contains hardly any air. The dough still rises. What process do you think happens to allow the bread to rise?

8 Draw a series of diagrams to show how one yeast cell will become three.

9 Choose one of the *foods* from the first picture on page 30 and find out how bacteria or fungi are used to help make it.

You should know...

- Microbes can be used to help make foods.
- Yeast is used in baking and brewing.
- Anaerobic respiration is respiration that does not need oxygen.
- The growth of a population is controlled by limiting factors (e.g. amount of food available).

What diseases are caused by microbes and how are they spread?

Microbes are all around us. Most are harmless, but some have unpleasant effects, like making food go bad or milk go sour. Some cause **diseases**.

You can usually tell that you have a disease by the effects it has on your body. These effects are known as the **symptoms** of the disease.

 1 'Colds' are a common disease caused by viruses. Write down two symptoms of a cold.

! *There are bacteria all over your body and you can never get rid of them! Bacteria in the armpits cause body odour (BO). The photograph shows an experiment to try to find out which deodorant works best.*

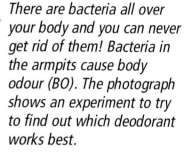

This table shows you some diseases and their symptoms.

Diseases caused by viruses	
Flu (short for influenza)	High temperature (**fever**), sore throat, aches
Measles	Fever, red eyes, flat red spots on face and chest (more on the face)
Chickenpox	Fever, raised red spots with yellow tops found on face and chest (more on chest)
Diseases caused by bacteria	
Food poisoning	Vomiting, stomach pain, diarrhoea
Impetigo	Blisters cover the face and chest which leave yellow scabs
Syphilis	A pale red rash covers the whole body
Tuberculosis (TB)	Fever, tiredness, coughing up blood
Diseases caused by fungi	
Athlete's foot	Skin between the toes is red, itchy and peeling
Thrush (caused by yeast)	White patches in the mouth or vagina

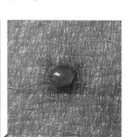

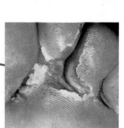

 2 Name one disease caused by:
  a) a fungus
  b) a virus
  c) a bacterium.

3 a) What are the symptoms of food poisoning?
  b) Find out the name of one bacterium that can cause food poisoning.

4 Many diseases cause a 'fever'. What is a fever?

Diseases that can be spread from person to person (or from animal to person) are called **infectious** diseases. These diseases are spread in many different ways.

Air

When someone coughs or sneezes, a spray of tiny watery droplets enters the air. These droplets may contain microbes. If someone else breathes in the droplets they may become **infected** by the microbes and get a disease. Colds, flu, chickenpox, measles and TB are all spread in this way.

Touch

Some diseases are passed on by touching an infected person (e.g. impetigo). Athlete's foot can be spread by touch or indirectly, by treading barefoot on a wet floor where an infected person has recently trodden.

Water

Cholera is a disease caused by a bacterium that is found in dirty water.

Food

Food poisoning is caused by bacteria found in food. The bacteria are usually killed by cooking.

Animals

Some microbes are carried by animals. For example, mosquitoes carry the microbes that cause malaria and yellow fever.

Sex

Some diseases are passed on when people have sex. Syphilis is an example.

Special photography can show up the droplets in a sneeze. The droplets in a sneeze may come out of your nose at 100 km/h.

5 What is an infectious disease?

6 Name a disease spread through the air, caused by:
a) a virus b) a bacterium.

7 Name a disease spread by touch, caused by:
a) a bacterium b) a fungus.

Cholera is often found in regions hit by a natural disaster when sewage gets into clean water supplies. The photograph shows people in Sahapur, West Bengal, just after floods in September 2000.

8 a) What sort of microbe is cholera caused by?
b) Why do you think cholera occurs in areas hit by disasters?

9 When a doctor works out what is wrong with someone, he or she is said to make a **diagnosis**. Imagine you are a doctor and three people come to see you. Their photos are shown below.
a) What diagnosis would you make for each of your patients, A, B and C?
b) Suggest how each person may have got their disease.

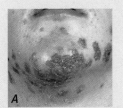
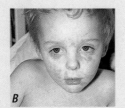
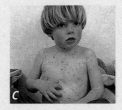

10 Find out which of the diseases on this page people in central Africa get. Design a leaflet to show travellers to Africa how to avoid these diseases.

You should know...

● The name of a disease caused by each of the different sorts of microbes.

● The different ways diseases can be spread.

How did John Snow work out how cholera was spread?

Cholera is an infectious disease which causes very bad diarrhoea and vomiting. In the nineteenth century, cholera killed many people.

Dr John Snow made careful **observations** of where and how infected people lived. He found that people with the disease often had a different water supply from their neighbours who remained healthy. He came up with a **theory** that cholera was spread in the water. A theory is a scientific idea that can be tested. He thought that something inside infected people came out in their faeces and if the faeces got into the water, other people caught the disease.

1 Why did Snow think that cholera was spread by water?

2 William Farr had a theory that cholera was caused by 'bad air'. Why do you think Snow didn't believe this theory?

In 1854 nearly 500 people died in ten days in an area around Broad Street in London. In those days, people in this area got water from pumps in the streets. Snow marked the deaths on a map and also drew in the positions of the pumps.

He **predicted** that if people stopped using the Broad Street pump, they would stop getting cholera. He got the pump handle removed, and soon afterwards, people did stop getting cholera. This provided more **evidence** that his theory was right.

People started to believe Snow's theory, but it wasn't until 1883 that the bacterium that causes cholera was found.

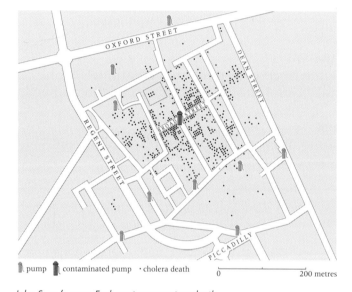

🖈 pump 🖈 contaminated pump · cholera death   0 ———— 200 metres

John Snow's map. Each spot represents a death.

A replica of the pump now outside the John Snow pub in Broadwick Street (which used to be called Broad Street). Notice that it has no handle.

3 a) What is a theory?
   b) What evidence supported Snow's theory? Use the map to help you.

4 Why do you think cholera occurs in refugee camps?

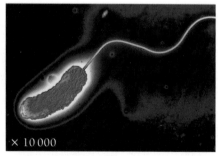

× 10 000

The bacterium Vibrio cholerae causes cholera.

You should know...
● **What a theory is.**

How do we stop the spread of diseases?

In the middle of the nineteenth century, cities smelled disgusting. Sewage was often stored in cellars (cesspits) under houses or flowed into the streets where it collected in small ditches in the road. The sewage often leaked into the water supply.

Diseases were very common; poor workmen in London often died before reaching the age of 20! After it was discovered that the sewage in drinking water caused diseases, sewer tunnels were built and water was used to wash the sewage away. This greatly reduced the number of people with diseases.

Proper sewage disposal was the most important development in stopping people dying from diseases. Today, we also try to kill microbes or stop them growing.

Method	Used to ...	Prevents the spread of ...
Pasteurisation	pasteurise milk (heated up to 70 °C for about 15 seconds which kills harmful bacteria)	tuberculosis
Disinfectants	kill bacteria in toilets and around buildings	stomach upsets, legionnaire's disease
Soaps and **antiseptics** (found in toothpaste and antiperspirants)	kill bacteria on our bodies	skin diseases, stomach upsets
Adding chlorine to drinking water supplies	kill harmful bacteria in the water	cholera, typhoid, stomach upsets
Salting, canning, pickling in vinegar	kill bacteria and fungi in food	stomach upsets
Drying, freezing, refrigeration	stop or slow down the growth of bacteria and fungi in food	stomach upsets
Cooking foods well	kill off bacteria	food poisoning

! A sewer tunnel designed in 1858 by Isambard Kingdom Brunel went under the Thames. Queen Victoria liked it so much that she asked for a railway to be put in it. It never became a sewer and today it is part of the Bakerloo Underground line!

P Bacteria can be grown on a jelly called agar. How could you find out if washing with soap helps to remove bacteria? Or is plain water just as good?

?
1 Why do you think building sewers reduced the number of people with diseases?

2 Make a list of all the ways in which bacteria have been stopped from getting to you so far today.

3 a) What is pasteurisation?
   b) Why do you think pasteurisation has helped to make tuberculosis a much less common disease?

You should know...
● **Methods of killing bacteria.**

How does your body protect you against diseases?

Your body has ways of killing microbes and stopping them getting inside you. These are your **natural defences**.

A chemical in your tears kills bacteria.

Hairs in your nose trap some microbes and a sticky substance called **mucus** is produced which microbes get stuck to.

Skin helps to keep microbes out of the body; if you cut yourself, a clot (a **scab**) forms to stop microbes getting in.

Acid in your stomach kills microbes.

Cells in your windpipe **(trachea)** also produce mucus. **Ciliated epithelial cells** sweep the mucus and trapped microbes to the top of your gullet to be swallowed.

cilia
This cell produces mucus.
ciliated epithelial cell

White blood cells destroy microbes; some of them surround (**engulf**) microbes.

Other white blood cells make **antibodies**. These stick to microbes, making it easier for them to be engulfed. Antibodies can also make the microbes stick together or burst open. However, antibodies have to be specially made to attach to each different sort of microbe and this takes time.

The white blood cells of babies are not as good at fighting microbes as those of older children. Breastfeeding can help since breast milk contains antibodies.

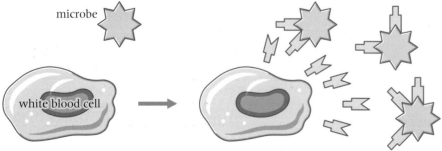

microbe

white blood cell

The white blood cell finds a microbe and starts to make antibodies.

The antibodies are made specially to fit onto the outside of the microbe. Each type of microbe has a different surface and so needs a different type of antibody.

?

1 Why is it important for a scab to form quickly?

2 a) What is mucus?
 b) What does it do?
 c) Name two places where it is produced.

3 a) List three things antibodies can do to microbes.
 b) Why does it take time for antibodies to be produced?

4 Antibodies are said to be 'specific' for a certain microbe. What do you think this means?

You should know...

● **How natural defences protect you from microbes.**

● **How white blood cells destroy microbes.**

How does immunisation work?

If you get **infected** with microbes, they reproduce. It takes time for your body to make antibodies and so you get the disease until there are enough antibodies in your blood to destroy all the microbes.

When you have recovered from a disease, some antibodies stay in your blood, often forever. This means that your body is ready for that particular microbe if it infects you again. You will not get that disease again and you are said to be **immune**.

Injections which contain a **vaccine** protect us from diseases. Giving these injections is called **immunisation** and it makes the body produce antibodies against a microbe.

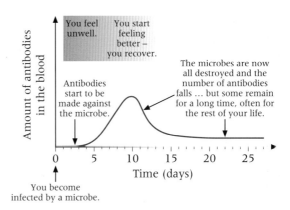

> **1** What does it mean if someone is immune to a disease?

Age of person	Vaccine given
2–4 months	Diphtheria, whooping cough, polio, tetanus, bacterial meningitis
1–2 years	Measles, mumps, rubella
3–5 years	Diphtheria, tetanus, polio
10–14 years (girls only)	Rubella
13 years	Tuberculosis
16–19 years	Tetanus, polio
Adults	Tetanus every 5–10 years

Normal ages for immunisations in the UK. You need some immunisations more than once: this is to make sure that your body builds up high enough levels of antibodies. The extra injections are called 'boosters'.

A vaccine contains the microbes that normally cause a disease but which have been treated to stop them doing this. Your body produces antibodies against the treated microbes. Many of these stay in your blood ready to help destroy the real microbes quickly if you ever become infected by them. You become immune to the disease. Antibodies can pass from mother to baby through the placenta and breast milk. This helps the baby to fight infections.

> **2** Sketch a graph to show the changes in the number of antibodies after an immunisation.
>
> **3** Chickenpox and measles are caused by viruses.
> a) Explain why you can only get chickenpox once.
> b) If you have had chickenpox, will it stop you from getting measles? Explain your answer.
> c) How can you make sure you never get measles?

Edward Jenner (1749–1823) invented vaccines. He gave people a mild disease called cowpox to stop them getting smallpox (a very nasty disease). Thanks to immunisation smallpox no longer exists. The last case was in Africa in 1978.

A child with smallpox.

You should know...
- **Why immunisations are given.**

How do antibiotics work?

Vaccines cannot be made for every disease but **medicines** can help treat and cure many diseases.

Antibiotics are medicines that harm bacteria. They were discovered by Alexander Fleming in 1928 when he looked at some bacteria growing on agar jelly. A mould had also grown on the agar, and Fleming observed that the bacteria were not growing near the mould.

Fleming came up with a theory that the mould produced a chemical which harmed the bacteria. He was right and, along with two other scientists (Howard Florey and Ernst Chain), made the first antibiotic – penicillin. There are now many different antibiotics, and different ones harm different bacteria. Bacteria that are not harmed by an antibiotic are said to be **resistant** to it.

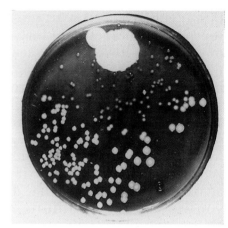

One of Fleming's Petri dishes. The mould is at the top; notice that the clumps of bacteria only grow well far away from the mould.

 Bacteria can be grown in Petri dishes containing agar. Antibiotics can be tested by soaking disks of paper in antibiotics and putting the disks on the agar. How would you test three antibiotics against a bacterium called *E. coli*? How would you tell which was the best antibiotic?

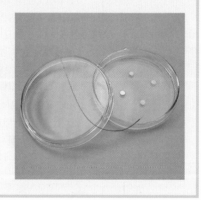

1 What are antibiotics?

2 a) What theory did Fleming come up with?
 b) What evidence supported this theory?

3 What does it mean if a bacterium is resistant to an antibiotic?

4 Why can't colds be cured by antibiotics?

5 What does aspirin do?

6 Find out why Fleming named his antibiotic penicillin.

 The skins of toads produce their own antibiotics.

Antibiotics don't work against viruses. When a disease is caused by a virus you can usually only ease the symptoms. If you have a fever, **medicines** like aspirin and paracetamol can reduce your temperature and help stop you aching.

Other medicines can treat problems not caused by microbes, like cancer, indigestion and travel sickness.

You should know...

● **What antibiotics are used for.**

What is AIDS and how is it spread?

AIDS stands for **A**cquired **I**mmune **D**eficiency **S**yndrome and is caused by the **H**uman **I**mmunodeficiency **V**irus (**HIV**).

AIDS is a killer disease with no cure and no vaccine. Around the world there are 16 000 new infections every day. People in Africa are particularly badly affected.

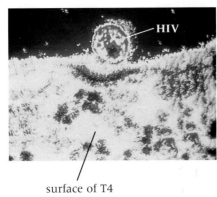

surface of T4 lymphocyte

People with the virus are **HIV positive**. HIV infects white blood cells called **T4 lymphocytes**, which are vital for destroying microbes in the body. The virus gets into the cells, and DNA from it is inserted into the cell's DNA.

The HIV DNA causes the lymphocytes to **replicate** (make new copies of) the virus. These burst out of the cell and destroy it.

Over many years the number of HIV viruses increases. Eventually, so many T4 lymphocytes are destroyed that the person gets many other diseases, and is said to have AIDS. It is these other diseases that kill the person.

HIV is spread through sex and by drug addicts sharing needles. HIV-positive pregnant mothers can also pass it on to their unborn babies. It cannot be passed on by coming into normal contact with an HIV-positive person. Using a condom during sex stops the virus from passing from person to person.

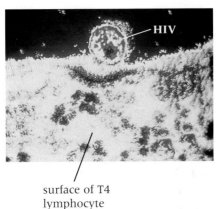

The lymphocyte may divide.

The cell makes new viruses.

The viruses burst out of the cell.

1 Explain how millions of T4 lymphocytes can get infected with the virus if only one gets into the body.

2 Why might a person with AIDS die from a disease caused by a bacterium?

3 a) How is HIV spread?
   b) How can its spread be stopped?

4 Why do you think HIV has the name it does?

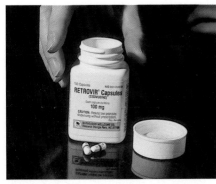

There are anti-HIV medicines, like zidovudine. These stop the virus from infecting too many new cells but they are not a cure.

Why are there differences between organisms?

The place where an organism lives is called a **habitat**.

A woodland habitat.

A pond habitat.

 1 Look at the photographs of the habitats. For *each* habitat, suggest the names of:
a) two animals that live there
b) two plants that live there.

In every habitat there are non-living factors, like the temperature, how wet it is and the amount of light. These are called **physical environmental factors**. All the physical environmental factors in a habitat are called the **environment** of that habitat.

2 Describe the environment in *each* of the habitats in the photographs.

In order for an animal to survive in a habitat, it needs food, water, oxygen and shelter. It also needs to find a mate to reproduce. Plants need light, water and carbon dioxide to make their food. They also need nutrients (mineral salts), oxygen and space to grow.

Each organism in a habitat has features that allow it to live and reproduce in that habitat. For example, a fish has gills to allow it to take oxygen out of the water. We say that organisms are **adapted** to their habitats.

3 Why don't fish have lungs?

4 Draw a table like the one below. The table should show how different plants and animals get the things they need to survive in different habitats. Complete the table for each of the organisms you named in question 1.

Name of organism	Name of habitat	What it needs	How it gets the things it needs

You should know...

● Organisms are adapted to survive in the environments found in their habitats.

How are animals put into groups?

Scientists sort living organisms into groups. This is called **classification**. The largest sets are called kingdoms. The biggest kingdoms are the **animal kingdom** and the **plant kingdom**.

There are many different types of organisms in each kingdom, so each is divided into smaller groups. The animal kingdom can be divided into two smaller groups – animals with a backbone are called **vertebrates** and animals without a backbone are called **invertebrates**. Each of these can be divided into even smaller groups.

1 What do scientists call grouping things together?

2 What are kingdoms?

3 Which are the two largest kingdoms?

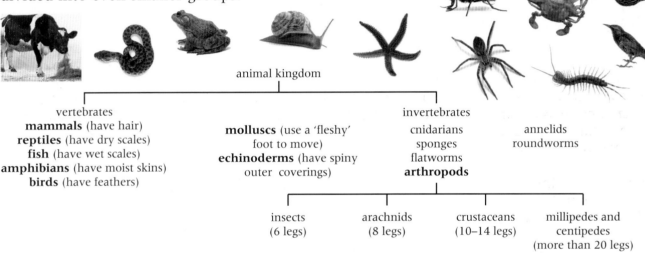

animal kingdom

vertebrates
mammals (have hair)
reptiles (have dry scales)
fish (have wet scales)
amphibians (have moist skins)
birds (have feathers)

molluscs (use a 'fleshy' foot to move)
echinoderms (have spiny outer coverings)

invertebrates
cnidarians
sponges
flatworms
arthropods

annelids
roundworms

insects
(6 legs)

arachnids
(8 legs)

crustaceans
(10–14 legs)

millipedes and centipedes
(more than 20 legs)

The name **arthropod** means jointed legs. This group is divided into four smaller groups, based on the number of legs. All arthropods have a hard outer covering called an **exoskeleton**.

The animal kingdom – the most important groups to know are in bold type.

4 Look at the photographs of organisms in the animal kingdom. Write down which group each one belongs to.

5 What are animals without backbones called?

6 For each of these lists of organisms, write down which is the odd one out and why.
   a) lizard   crocodile   toad   snake   tortoise
   b) wasp   bee   butterfly   crab   beetle

7 What does the name arthropod mean?

8 What is an exoskeleton?

You should know...

- **The main groups in the animal kingdom.**
- **The main features of the five vertebrate groups.**
- **The main features of arthropods, echinoderms and molluscs.**

How are plants put into groups?

The **plant kingdom** is another large group of organisms. All the organisms in this kingdom make their own food (glucose) using **photosynthesis**. Plants need water and carbon dioxide as raw materials and light energy to make photosynthesis happen.

> **?** **1** What do all organisms in the plant kingdom have in common?
>
> **2** What is the name of the process by which plants make their own food?

The two main features that are used to put plants into smaller groups are:
- whether they produce **seeds** or not
- whether they have tissues to transport water and other substances or not.

There are four main plant groups: **mosses**, **ferns**, **conifers** and **flowering plants**.

Conifers and flowering plants reproduce using seeds. Each seed can grow into a new plant.

Mosses and ferns reproduce using tiny **spores**. Each spore can grow into a new plant. Spores are so small you can hardly see them.

Conifer seeds are found inside **cones**.

The seeds of flowering plants are found inside **fruits**.

Moss spores are made inside capsules.

Ferns have spore containers on the undersides of their leaves.

> **?** **3** What are the two main features used to group plants?
>
> **4** Look at the four pictures on the right.
> a) Write down one way in which mosses and ferns are similar.
> b) Write down two differences between conifers and flowering plants.

Most plants absorb water from the soil using **roots** and transport it up through the plant to the leaves in special tubes called **xylem vessels** (pronounced '*z-eye-lem*').

Other tissues (**phloem**) carry other substances around the plant.

Plants with xylem vessels have waterproof layers of waxy **cuticle** on their leaves to stop them losing too much water.

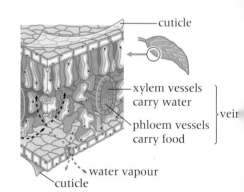

cuticle
xylem vessels carry water
vein
phloem vessels carry food
water vapour
cuticle

Conifers have roots and xylem vessels. They have needle-shaped leaves with cuticles.

Flowering plants have roots and xylem vessels. They have large flat leaves with cuticles. Most plants are flowering plants, but some of the flowers are difficult to spot. For example, grass is a flowering plant – grass flowers are green and not brightly coloured.

Mosses do not have roots or xylem vessels. They have thin leaves with no cuticle which lose a lot of water.

Ferns have roots and xylem vessels. They have many small leaves that have cuticles and don't lose much water.

! *Trees can be conifers or flowering plants. The tallest flowering plants in the world are Eucalyptus trees in Tasmania. They can grow up to 150 m tall.*

P How could you develop a classification system to group plants that live in and around water?
- How will you find information about the plants' features?

? 5 a) What do xylem vessels do?
   b) Which plant groups have xylem vessels?

6 Why do mosses grow best in damp places?

7 Write down the names of the four plant groups. For each group, make a list of its features. You can draw pictures if you wish.

P How could you find out which type of leaf loses the least water?
- Which leaves would you use?
- What would you measure?

You should know...

- The main features of mosses, ferns, conifers and flowering plants, and how they reproduce.

- Plants make their own food using energy from the Sun in a process called photosynthesis.

How can we collect data to answer questions about a habitat?

An **ecologist** is a scientist who studies habitats. Ecologists find out what different types of organisms live in a particular habitat. All the animals and plants that live in a habitat make up a **community**. Different habitats will have different communities.

Within a community, the total number of individuals of one species is called a **population**. Ecologists often need to find out the size of each population, so that they can detect any changes. If a population does change, they try to find out why.

1 Write down the meanings of the following words.
  a) ecologist
  b) community
  c) population

2 Look at the picture.
  a) What sort of habitat is this?
  b) List the organisms in the community.
  c) What is the population of minnows?

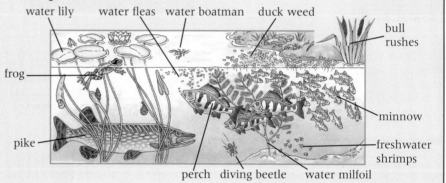

water lily   water fleas   water boatman   duck weed   bull rushes   frog   pike   minnow   freshwater shrimps   perch   diving beetle   water milfoil

Counting organisms may be difficult if there are large numbers of them or they are hard to find. For these reasons, small areas are looked at rather than a whole habitat. We say that we take **samples** from a habitat. From the number of individuals in the sample, scientists can **estimate** how many there are altogether. For example, to estimate the number of daisy plants in a lawn, you could count the number in 1 m². If the lawn is 100 m², multiply the number of daisies in 1 m² by 100 to get the total.

*A **quadrat** is a square used to count the number of plants in a small area. It is thrown randomly about the habitat. Each time it lands the plants inside it are counted.*

Different ways of sampling

More than one sample should be taken because organisms are not spread evenly over a habitat. Different organisms prefer different environments and so have an **uneven distribution**.

***Tree beating** is used to collect animals that live in trees or bushes. A branch is shaken or hit and the animals fall onto the sheet or tray beneath.*

3 There are 46 daisy plants in 2 m² of a lawn. Estimate the total number in 100 m².

*A **sweepnet** is used to collect small animals found in long grass. It is a strongnet that is swept through the grass several times.*

*A sample of leaves can be put into a **Tullgren funnel**. The small animals move away from heat and light and fall into the beaker where they can be examined and counted. After counting they are returned to where they were collected.*

Pond dipping involves putting a small net or jar into various parts of a pond.

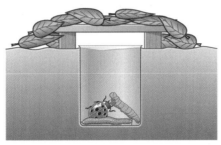

*A **pitfall trap** is a jar buried in the ground and left. Various small animals will fall into it and become trapped. The lid stops rain getting in.*

P How could you use a quadrat to estimate how many steel tacks have been buried in a tray of sand?
- How will you remove the tacks without disturbing the sand?
- How many quadrat samples will you take?

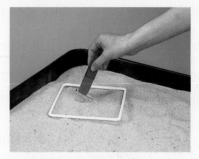

*A **quadrat** is a sampling square.*

Besides information about living organisms, ecologists also need to collect data about the physical environmental factors in a habitat. For example: temperature variations, light intensity, how moist the atmosphere is (**humidity**) and how much oxygen is dissolved in the water.

! *In the Sahara desert a temperature of 58 °C was recorded in the shade during September 1922. During the night, temperatures may fall below freezing in the winter. Not many organisms can survive those extremes!*

? 4 a) What is a quadrat?
   b) Which sampling technique would you use to collect animals that live in trees?
   c) Which would you use to collect small animals that crawl along the ground?
   d) What is pond dipping?

5 Make a list of the physical environmental factors that you could measure in a habitat.

You should know...
- How to collect data about a habitat.
- There are different ways of taking samples to estimate the size of a population (e.g. using a quadrat).
- Different habitats support different communities of organisms.

Why do different organisms live in different environments?

When ecologists study a habitat they try to disturb it as little as possible. They do not remove plants and if they remove small animals to examine they always return them to where they were found. Often they have to turn over logs or stones to look for small animals. These are always replaced. They also have to be very careful not to damage any animals that they collect. A good way of doing this is to use a **pooter**.

Sucking on this tube draws small animals into the container.

collecting tube

A pooter.

1 Make up a list of rules for ecologists to follow when investigating a habitat.

2 Look carefully at the photograph of the pooter.
a) Why don't the small animals get sucked into the boy's mouth?
b) Pooters are never used to collect animals that are the same size or bigger than the collecting tube. Suggest why.

Ecologists often have to identify the organisms that they find. They use books, called field guides, and keys. The diagram shows part of a key used to identify butterflies and moths. It has been used to identify the moth in the photograph above.

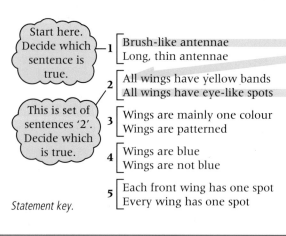

Start here. Decide which sentence is true.

1 Brush-like antennae — go to **2**
   Long, thin antennae — go to **3**

The top sentence is true. Now go to set of sentences '2'.

2 All wings have yellow bands — *Lasiocampa quercus*
   All wings have eye-like spots — *Saturnio emperor*

This is set of sentences '2'. Decide which is true.

This is the true sentence. The answer is *Saturnia emperor*.

3 Wings are mainly one colour — go to **4**
   Wings are patterned — go to **6**

4 Wings are blue — *Polyommatus icarus*
   Wings are not blue — go to **5**

5 Each front wing has one spot — *Pieris rapae*
   Every wing has one spot — *Gonepteryx rhamni*

Statement key.

3 Use the key to identify insect A.

4 The key is not complete. Add two sentences for number '6' to tell the difference between insects B and C.

A

B

C

After ecologists have investigated a habitat they need to tell others about their findings. They do this by writing a report, called a paper, or displaying a poster or giving a talk.

The reports written by ecologists are often about how environmental factors affect what plants and animals are living in a certain area. They also try to find links between the environmental factors. For example, fast-flowing water is normally colder than still water because the Sun does not get as much chance to warm it up.

P How would you find out if there was a link between the amount of light and the temperature in different environments?
- What equipment would you use?
- How would you find out if other environmental factors were affecting the temperature?

Ecologists also investigate the special features that organisms have to allow them to survive in an environment. All organisms are **adapted** to their environments. Bladder wrack is a kind of seaweed. It has adaptations to help it live in rock pools near the sea.

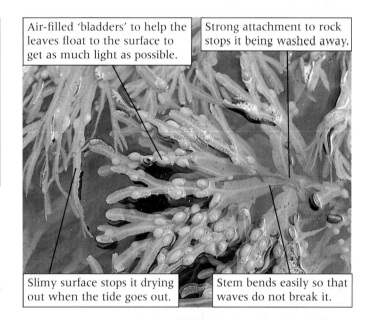

Air-filled 'bladders' to help the leaves float to the surface to get as much light as possible.

Strong attachment to rock stops it being washed away.

Slimy surface stops it drying out when the tide goes out.

Stem bends easily so that waves do not break it.

Members of the same community often have similar adaptations to cope with their environment. For example, many plants and animals that live in fast-flowing rivers are adapted for holding on to rocks and stones to stop them being washed away.

5 a) What process does bladder wrack use to make its own food?
   b) How is bladder wrack adapted to do this?

6 Suggest reasons for the following.
   a) Duckweed plants float on the surface of ponds. They are not found in rivers.
   b) Plants that live in fast rivers have flexible stems.
   c) There are more free-swimming animals in ponds.
   d) Plants with roots only grow at the edges of deep ponds, not in the middle.

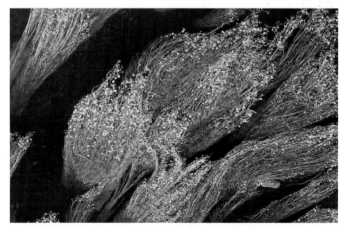

You should know...
- Different habitats contain different communities because organisms are adapted to live in certain environments.

Why do populations change in a habitat?

The reports written by ecologists are often about where organisms can be found in a habitat (their **distribution**). The distribution of an organism is often affected by environmental factors. For example, in a wood some small plants will only grow where there are gaps between the trees and there is more light.

1 Woodlice feed on wet, rotting dead leaves and wood.
   a) Name one environmental factor that is needed for wood to rot.
   b) Name two places in a wood where you would expect to find woodlice.

2 If organisms are only found in certain places, their distribution is said to be uneven.
   a) Name two animals which you would expect to be unevenly distributed in a wood. Explain you answer.
   b) Name one organism which you would expect to be evenly distributed in a wood. Explain you answer.

In any habitat, an animal needs certain resources. For example, an animal has to find a mate, a source of food and space in which to live and protect itself. The distribution of an organism depends on how easy it is to get these resources.

Aphids feed off the sugary liquid inside the phloem vessels in plant stems by inserting a long tube into the stem. However, the trunks of trees are too thick and strong for them to push the tube in and so aphids are only found on the younger branches and leaf stems of trees.

The sizes of populations are changed by the number of births and the number of deaths. If the things that an organism needs are in short supply, some will die and their numbers will fall. When there is a good supply of the things that an organism needs, more will survive.

3 Squirrels live in trees, in nests called dreys. Suggest why squirrels are not found on grassy hills.

When there is more food around, more animals are born and more of the new-born animals survive. In Northern Canada snowshoe hares are eaten by lynxes. When there are lots of hares, the lynxes have lots to eat. They reproduce successfully and their population increases. In years when there are less hares, the lynx population also decreases – many of them starve.

Organisms **compete** with one another. *Animals* compete for food and space in a habitat. *Plants* compete for light, water and nutrients (mineral salts). The organisms with the best **adaptations** for **competition** are more likely to survive and reproduce. The others may die.

Death can be caused by starvation, disease, old age or by being eaten. An animal that eats another is called a **predator**. The animal that it eats is its **prey**.

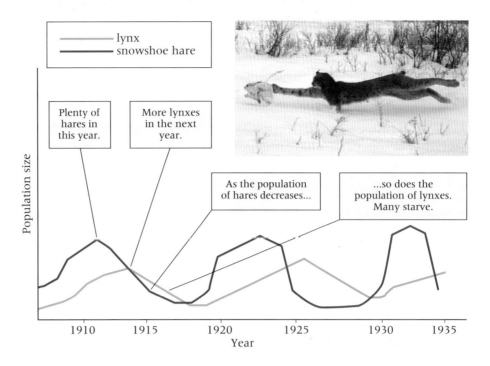

— lynx
— snowshoe hare

Population size

Plenty of hares in this year.

More lynxes in the next year.

As the population of hares decreases...

...so does the population of lynxes. Many starve.

1910   1915   1920   1925   1930   1935
Year

Daisies, dandelions and plantains are weeds. How would you estimate the population of each type of weed on your school playing field?
- How would you do your sampling?
- How would you work out your estimate?
- How would you work out which of these weeds is the most 'successful'?

4 Look at the graph of the snowshoe hare and lynx populations.
   a) Which animal is the predator and which is the prey?
   b) Name one thing that might increase the hare population.
   c) List three things that might decrease the lynx population.

5 What do plants compete for?

6 Name one adaptation that might allow one lynx to survive when another one starves.

7 Woodlice are eaten by shrews (small mouse-like creatures).
   a) Suggest where you might find shrews in a wood.
   b) Name two other resources that a shrew needs.
   c) Suggest one environmental factor that might affect the size of the shrew population. Write down how a change in this factor would change the population size.

You should know...
- **What affects the distribution and the population size of an organism.**
- **Organisms with the best adaptations for competition survive best.**

How do changes in a food web affect populations?

A **food web** is a collection of food chains showing what eats what in a habitat.

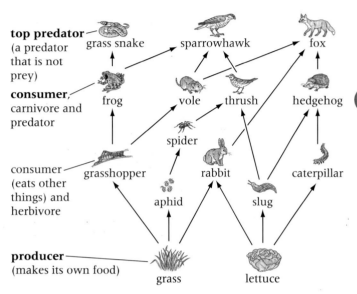

top predator
(a predator
that is not
prey)

consumer,
carnivore and
predator

consumer
(eats other
things) and
herbivore

producer
(makes its own food)

grass snake   sparrowhawk   fox

frog   vole   thrush   hedgehog

spider

grasshopper   rabbit   caterpillar

aphid   slug

grass   lettuce

Humans are often the top predators in food chains but we eat some odd things. Most people eat about eight spiders during their lives while asleep.

1 a) What do foxes eat?
   b) Write down the longest food chain in the web.
   c) Write a list of the organisms in the longest food chain. Describe what each is by writing one or more of these words next to it:
       carnivore   consumer   herbivore   omnivore   producer   top predator
   d) Badgers eat insects and fruit. Which of the words in part c) describes a badger?

If the population of one organism changes, the numbers of many of the other organisms in the food web may also change. For example, if the rabbits get a disease and die, there will be more grass. The population of the grasshoppers may then increase.

Organisms depend on one another for things besides food. Birds need trees for shelter. Plants use animal waste to help them grow, since the waste contains mineral salts. Mineral salts are also put into the soil when dead organisms rot. Many plants need insects to carry pollen from flower to flower.

2 Use the food web to predict what would happen to the number of slugs in each of these situations.
   a) The caterpillars all die.
   b) There is no rain for a long time.
   c) The spiders all die.

3 Manure is the waste produced by farm animals. Explain why gardeners put manure on their soil.

4 Squirrels often hide piles of nuts (which contain seeds) to feed on over the winter but forget where they have hidden them. Explain why you think squirrels are helpful to trees.

You should know...

● **How to make predictions about population changes using a food web.**

● **That plants and animals depend on each other for things other than food.**

What are pyramids of numbers?

The first consumer in a food chain is the **primary consumer**. The second is the **secondary consumer** and the third is the **tertiary consumer**. As you go along a food chain, there are fewer and fewer individuals at each level. Hundreds of lettuce plants will only feed a small number of rabbits. A small number of rabbits will only feed one fox. A **pyramid of numbers** shows this. The lengths of the bars show the numbers of each organism.

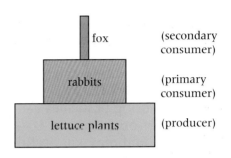

fox — (secondary consumer)

rabbits — (primary consumer)

lettuce plants — (producer)

> **1** Think up another food chain and sketch a pyramid of numbers for it.

A lot of the chemical energy in the food is used for respiration, to allow the rabbit to move, keep warm, etc.

Only some of the chemical energy is used for growth. Only the chemical energy inside the rabbit can be passed on to the fox.

A lot of the chemical energy is passed out in undigested food.

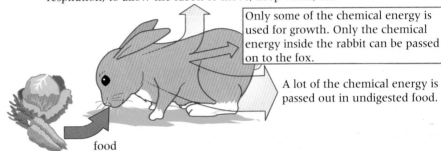

food

Normally there are fewer and fewer organisms as you go along a food chain because energy is lost at each stage. Of all the **chemical energy** in an animal's food, only a small amount is stored in new materials as the animal grows.

> **2** Why do organisms respire?

Not all pyramids of numbers look like the one shown above. Pyramids can have odd shapes if the organisms are very different in size. A rose bush is very big and has a lot of energy stored in it. Many aphids can feed on it.

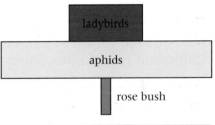

ladybirds

aphids

rose bush

> **3** Explain why this pyramid of numbers is an odd shape.
>
>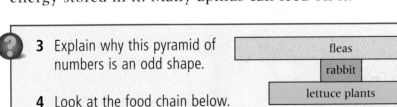
>
> fleas
>
> rabbit
>
> lettuce plants
>
> **4** Look at the food chain below.
>
> grass ⟶ grasshopper ⟶ frog ⟶ grass snake
> 100 000   500   5   1
>
> a) Sketch a pyramid of numbers for the food chain.
> b) Write down the names of:
>   i)   the top predator   ii) the consumers
>   iii) the producer   iv) the primary consumer
>   v)   the tertiary consumer vi) the herbivore
>   vii) the carnivores.

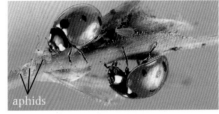

aphids

You should know...

● How to draw and understand pyramids of numbers.

● Energy is lost from a food chain at each stage.

How do people damage food webs?

Animals, especially insects, that eat crops are called **pests**. To stop this happening farmers often use chemicals, called **pesticides**, to kill them. However, using pesticides can affect other organisms in a food web, and may kill useful animals as well as the pests.

Some pesticides can also get passed up a food chain. In the 1940s a pesticide called DDT was used. DDT is not destroyed when it gets into an organism (it is **persistent**). This means that DDT passes up food chains as organisms are eaten. In large amounts DDT is poisonous (**toxic**). The diagram shows what happened when DDT was sprayed on Clear Lake in California to kill mosquitoes.

 1 Look at this food web. A farmer has used a pesticide to kill the caterpillars on his apple trees.
   a) How will this affect the aphid population? Explain your answer.
   b) How will this affect the blackbird population? Explain your answer.

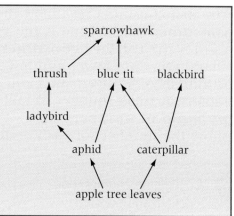

 A grebe eats many fish. It gets all the doses of DDT from all the fish it eats. The DDT kills the grebe.

 A fish eats many plankton. It gets many doses of DDT from the plankton but the fish does not die.

 Some of the DDT in the water gets into tiny plants called plankton.

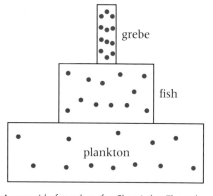

A pyramid of numbers for Clear Lake. The red dots represent doses of DDT. The poison gets more concentrated in animals as you go up the pyramid.

 2 What do the following words mean? Give an example of each.
   a) pest   b) pesticide

3 Look at the picture. It shows Minamata Bay in Japan. In the 1950s a plastics factory was putting poisonous mercury into the sea water.
   a) Draw a food chain using the organisms shown in the picture.
   b) Explain why about 70 people who lived along the shore died.

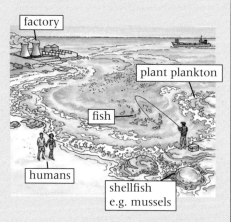

4 Why do you think Rachel Carson's book was called *Silent Spring*?

 In 1962 Rachel Carson warned people about the dangers of pesticides in her famous book, Silent Spring. Until that time, many people thought that pesticides were perfectly safe.

Extinction

What causes extinction and how can we stop it?

Many plants and animals have become **extinct**. This means that they have died out altogether. Scientists think that about one species a day becomes extinct. Dinosaurs became extinct 65 million years ago. It is thought that this was because the world suddenly got much colder. Extinction can be caused by:

- changes in the environment
- disease
- competition from other organisms that are better adapted
- human activities.

? **1** Introducing new fish into the Great Lakes helped to make the blue pike extinct. Explain why you think this happened.

EXTINCT

The Pyrenean ibex became extinct in January 2000 due to overhunting, disease and competition from goats and sheep.

EXTINCT

In 1888, to protect farmers' sheep, hunters in Tasmania were rewarded for killing thylacine. The last one died in a zoo in 1936.

EXTINCT

The blue pike, found in the Great Lakes of Canada, became extinct in 1975. The causes were overfishing, pollution and competition from new fish introduced into the lakes by settlers.

Animals and plants that are in danger of becoming extinct are called **endangered**.

ENDANGERED

Since the 1970s the black rhinoceros population in Africa has fallen by 95% due to hunting.

ENDANGERED

Since the 1970s the bluefin tuna population in the Atlantic Ocean has fallen by 70% due to overfishing.

ENDANGERED

The silversword plant from Hawaii is currently being eaten to extinction by sheep which were introduced by humans.

There are various ways in which endangered animals can be saved:

- protection of habitats by creating nature reserves
- breeding programmes in zoos and gardens
- making it illegal to hunt endangered animals and pick endangered plants.

? **2** a) What is a nature reserve?
   b) Make a list of five rules you would make for people visiting a nature reserve.

3 Try to find out why the Stephen Island wren became extinct.

4 The picture shows a dodo. Find out when and how it became extinct.

How many different materials are there?

The first people to study chemicals were known as alchemists. They tried to find magic ways to turn ordinary metals, like lead, into gold. They discovered that some substances could not be split into any simpler substances. They called these substances **elements**.

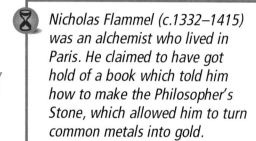

Nicholas Flammel (c.1332–1415) was an alchemist who lived in Paris. He claimed to have got hold of a book which told him how to make the Philosopher's Stone, which allowed him to turn common metals into gold.

Nicholas Flammel (kneeling).

 1 What is an element?

About 200 years ago, Alessandro Volta, an Italian scientist, invented the first battery. This gave scientists a new way to split up chemicals.

Potash is a chemical made from the ashes of log fires. It was thought to be an element because no-one had split it into anything simpler. In 1807, Sir Humphry Davy heated up some potash until it melted. He used one of Volta's batteries to pass an electric current through it and found that he produced a new metal. It was very soft and reacted very quickly with the air. He realised that he had found a new element. He called his new discovery **potassium**.

Volta's battery.

 2 Why did early scientists think that potash was an element?

3 a) Who showed that potash was not an element?

b) What element did this person get out of potash?

Volta demonstrating his battery.

Sir Humphry Davy (1778–1829).

Sir Humphry Davy used his new method to show that many other substances were not elements. One of these substances was lime. He obtained an element from lime in 1808 and called it **calcium** (from the Latin word for lime, calc).

Elements like gold and silver occur naturally in the ground, although they are very rare. Other elements can be obtained by heating some types of rock. Copper and tin can be obtained in this way. Most of the elements that we know about today can only be obtained from other materials by using heat and electricity. Aluminium and sodium are obtained by using electricity.

When you heat lime it glows with a bright white light. This was used in the theatre for spotlights, before electric lighting. The actor was said to be 'in the limelight' – a phrase that we still use today!

4 Name two elements which:
   a) occur naturally in the ground
   b) are easy to obtain from rocks.

5 Name four elements that were discovered using heat or electricity.

We now know of 115 different elements and they can be arranged on a large chart called the **Periodic Table** (see page 158). Most elements are **metals** and the others are called **non-metals**.

The elements are used to make all the materials in the Universe. That includes all the materials in us. So many different materials can be made that it is impossible to count them all. It is the way the elements are joined together that makes each material different. In a similar way, we can join the 26 letters of our alphabet together to make billions of different words. Chemists spend a lot of time getting elements to join together in different ways to make new materials.

other elements = 200 g

sulphur = 125 g

potassium = 175 g

phosphorus = 500 g

calcium = 1 kg

nitrogen = 1.5 kg

hydrogen = 5 kg

carbon = 9 kg

oxygen = 32.5 kg

human being
mass = 50 kg

6 Draw a bar chart to show the amounts of the different elements in a 50 kg human being.

7 The ancient Greeks thought that there were four elements: earth, air, fire and water. Which of these ancient elements best matches our modern words?
   a) solid   b) liquid
   c) gas   d) energy

You should know...

- That an element is a substance that cannot be split into any simpler substances.

What are elements made from?

The word 'elementary' means simple. **Elements** are simple substances. The particles that make up an element are called **atoms**. An atom is the smallest particle of an element that you can get.

You cannot split an element up into anything simpler using a chemical reaction. The silver in this jewellery is made up of atoms. As silver is an element, all the atoms in the jewellery are the same.

1 What is: a) an element   b) an atom?

2 The Periodic Table is a list of all the elements we know about. Use the Periodic Table on page 158 of the book to help you find out which five of the substances in this list are elements:

gold   salt   air   mercury   sulphur
water   oxygen   aluminium sand   chalk

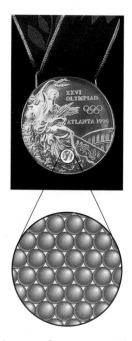

Gold is an element. All the atoms in the gold medal are the same.

Silver is also an element. The atoms in the silver medal are the same as each other, but different from the gold atoms.

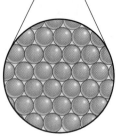

Bronze is *not* an element. Bronze is mostly copper, but also contains some tin. So, there are two different types of atoms in bronze. Bronze is a **mixture** of metals. Mixtures of metals are called **alloys**.

3 How many different kinds of atom are there in:
a) gold   b) silver   c) bronze?

4 'Silver' coins (like 10p pieces) are actually made of copper (75%) and nickel (25%).
Draw a particle diagram to show the arrangement of atoms in a 10p coin.

5 In what way are the bricks in these models like the atoms in a chemical element?

Each element has a **symbol**. Sometimes the symbol is the first letter of the name. The symbol for carbon is C and the one for oxygen is O. There are 115 elements and only 26 letters of the alphabet, so most elements have a two-letter code. For example, aluminium is Al and helium is He. The same chemical symbols are used all over the world. Sometimes the letters do not match the name in English, but are taken from other languages, usually Latin.

Leucippus and Democritus, two Greek scientists living 2500 years ago, first had the idea that an atom was the smallest possible particle that couldn't be split up. The Greek word 'atomos' means indivisible.

8 Some elements are named after famous scientists. Find out the names of the scientists who have had these elements named after them.
a) No   b) Es   c) Cm   d) Fm   e) Md.

P 'Bronze' coins (1p and 2p pieces) are now made of steel and coated with a thin layer of copper. New coins are magnetic, but older ones are not. How could you use a magnet to find out which year they changed from bronze to steel?

6 Look at the Periodic Table on page 158.
What are the symbols for these elements:
a) hydrogen   b) neon
c) nickel   d) silicon?

7 Look at the pictures below. Elements have different names in different languages.
Use the chemical symbols and the Periodic Table to work out the names of these elements in English.

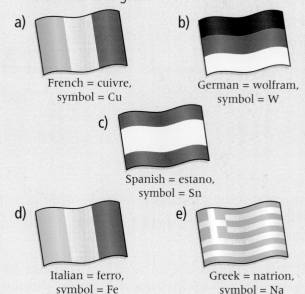

a) French = cuivre, symbol = Cu

b) German = wolfram, symbol = W

c) Spanish = estano, symbol = Sn

d) Italian = ferro, symbol = Fe

e) Greek = natrion, symbol = Na

You should know...

- Elements are simple substances which cannot be split into simpler ones by chemical reactions.

- Elements are made of atoms that are all the same.

- Each element has a chemical symbol.

Why is the Periodic Table arranged in the way that it is?

By the middle of the nineteenth century, about 60 elements were known. Scientists looked for ways to sort them; they searched for patterns in the elements' properties. Most elements were metals, but some were non-metals. Most were solids, a few were gases, and there were only two liquids (bromine and mercury).

A number of scientists tried to find a pattern. Johann Döbereiner looked for elements with similar properties in groups of three (triads).

Johann Döbereiner (1780–1849).

John Newlands (1837–1898).

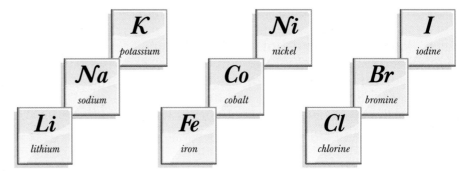

Some of Döbereiner's triads.

John Newlands thought he had found groups of seven elements, which he called his octaves, like the notes of a musical scale.

The elements didn't fit neatly into either pattern and whenever anyone discovered a new element, it threw the whole pattern out.

H	F	Cl
Li	Na	K
G	Mg	Ca
Bo	Al	Cr
C	Si	Ti
N	P	Mn
O	S	Fe

Some of Newlands' octaves. Glucinum (G) was the old name for beryllium.

1 Roughly how many elements were known by the middle of the nineteenth century?

2 a) Which scientist tried to group the elements in triads?
 b) Who tried to group them into octaves?
 c) What happened to these patterns when a new element was discovered?

Dimitri Mendeleev was a Russian chemist who enjoyed playing cards. He made a pack of cards using the elements, which he numbered from the lightest mass to the heaviest mass. On 17 February 1869 he sat down to play a game of patience, dealing out the cards to try to get a pattern so that similar elements came together in columns. The result of his card game was basically the table that we use today, which is called the **Periodic Table**. He did three important things:

- He didn't try to make a totally regular grid – some rows were longer than others.
- If the elements didn't fit his table, he swapped the cards round and told the experimenters that they must have got the masses of the elements wrong!
- He left gaps for elements that he said had not been discovered yet – and predicted what they would be like!

Dimitri Mendeleev (1834–1907).

Although his ideas were not totally correct, most of Mendeleev's predictions did come true, and his table of the elements was accepted as the best way of organising the elements. A modern version is shown on page 158. The photograph shows an earlier version, which stands in the Russian city of St Petersburg as a monument to his work.

A memorial to Mendeleev's achievement in St Petersburg, showing his original Periodic Table.

3 Compare Newlands' octaves with the modern Periodic Table.
  a) Which two elements have different symbols?
  b) Which elements have been discovered between hydrogen and iron since Newlands' time?

4 How could Mendeleev's table be used to predict the properties of elements that had not been discovered?

							H 1										**He** 4
Li 7	**Be** 9											**B** 11	**C** 12	**N** 14	**O** 16	**F** 19	**Ne** 20
Na 23	**Mg** 24											**Al** 27	**Si** 28	**P** 31	**S** 32	**Cl** 35	**Ar** 40
K 39	**Ca** 40	**Sc** 45	**Ti** 48	**V** 51	**Cr** 52	**Mn** 55	**Fe** 56	**Co** 59	**Ni** 59	**Cu** 64	**Zn** 65	**Ga** 70	**Ge** 73	**As** 75	**Se** 79	**Br** 80	**Kr** 84
Rb 85	**Sr** 88	**Y** 89	**Zr** 91	**Nb** 93	**Mo** 96	**Tc** 98	**Ru** 101	**Rh** 103	**Pd** 106	**Ag** 108	**Cd** 112	**In** 115	**Sn** 119	**Sb** 122	**Te** 128	**I** 127	**Xe** 131
Cs 133	**Ba** 137	**La** 139	**Hf** 178	**Ta** 181	**W** 184	**Re** 186	**Os** 190	**Ir** 192	**Pt** 195	**Au** 197	**Hg** 201	**Tl** 204	**Pb** 207	**Bi** 209	**Po** 209	**At** 210	**Rn** 222
Fr 223	**Ra** 226	**Ac** 227	**Rf** 261	**Db** 262	**Sg** 266	**Bh** 264	**Hs** 269	**Mt** 268	**Ds** 271	**Rg** 272	**Uub** 285	**Uut** 284	**Uuq** 289	**Uup** 288	**Uuh** 292		

Ce 140	**Pr** 141	**Nd** 144	**Pm** 145	**Sm** 150	**Eu** 152	**Gd** 157	**Tb** 159	**Dy** 163	**Ho** 165	**Er** 167	**Tm** 169	**Yb** 173	**Lu** 175
Th 232	**Pa** 231	**U** 238	**Np** 237	**Pu** 244	**Am** 243	**Cm** 247	**Bk** 247	**Cf** 251	**Es** 252	**Fm** 257	**Md** 258	**No** 259	**Lr** 262

The modern Periodic Table.

How can we tell if an element is a metal?

Most elements are **metals**. A few are not, and these are called **non-metals**. The objects in this photograph are all made of metal.

? **1** a) In what way do all the metals in the photograph look similar?

b) State one way in which they look different.

lead flashing

Lead is a metal but it is not shiny.

Many metals are **shiny**. But just looking at something is not always a good way to tell if is a metal. Some metals, like lead, can be quite dull. Some substances, like plastics, can look shiny even though they are not metals. You have to examine the **properties** of a substance to decide whether it is a metal or not.

To cook food, heat must travel through the saucepan. The saucepan is made of metal because it lets the heat pass through. One of the properties of metals is that they are good **heat conductors**. It is important that saucepans do not melt or burn when you heat them. Most metals are solids with a **high melting point**. They are quite difficult to melt. One exception is mercury. This is the only metal that is a liquid at room temperature.

? **2** Write down two reasons why a saucepan is usually made of metal.

Metals are also good **electrical conductors**. Inside this plug, the electric current will travel through the parts that are made of metal.

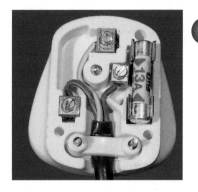

? **3** Why are the electrical wires around a house made of metal?

A few metals are **magnetic**. Most metals are not. Iron is the most common magnetic metal. A magnet can be used to sort iron objects from other metals, for example when recycling cans.

This machine sorts drinks cans depending on whether they are magnetic or not. Iron cans are magnetic. Aluminium cans are not magnetic.

? **4** Write down three properties that most metals have.

5 Look at the Periodic Table on page 158.
   a) On which side of the table do you find all the metals?
   b) The three magnetic elements are iron, cobalt and nickel. What do you notice about the position of these three elements in the table?
   c) Copper, silver and gold are metals that are used for jewellery. Where do these metals come in the table?

You should know...
- Metals are good conductors of heat and electricity.
- Most metals are shiny.
- Most metals are solids with a high melting point.
- A few metals, like iron, are magnetic.

Fire and brimstone

What are the properties of non-metals?

Only 22 of the elements are non-metals. Half of these are gases, and only one (bromine) is a liquid. The rest are solids. All of these elements are found on the right-hand side of the Periodic Table (see page 158).

One of the solid non-metals is **sulphur**. Sulphur is found naturally in areas where there are volcanoes. Its ancient name is brimstone. Sulphur melts quite easily. Like almost all non-metals it will not conduct heat or electricity.

Sulphur is found as a pure element, in the form of yellow crystals.

Phosphorus is a non-metal which burns easily. It can be set alight just by touching it with a warm rod. Phosphorus and sulphur used to be used in match heads. Rubbing the match head along the side of the box gave enough heat to set the match on fire. Scientists have now found alternatives to phosphorus and sulphur which are safer.

Phosphorus burning.

What tests could you carry out to decide if an element was a metal or a non-metal?
- How many tests would you need to do?
- Which results would be the most important?

1 How many elements are non-metals?

2 How many of the non-metals are:
a) gases b) liquids c) solids?

3 Where are the non-metals on the Periodic Table?

Iodine is another non-metal. At room temperature it is a solid. When you heat it gently it changes state and turns directly into a gas. Sulphur, phosphorus and iodine all change state quite easily when you heat them. They have **low melting points** and **low boiling points**.

Solid iodine.   Iodine gas.

> **4** a) What is the state of iodine at room temperature?
> b) What state does it change to when it is heated?
> c) Why is this unusual?

Chlorine is a poisonous gas. You can detect chlorine by its smell and by its green colour. We use chlorine in bleaches, and as a disinfectant in swimming pools. Scientists need to carry out careful tests to ensure that the levels of chlorine in the water are just enough to kill harmful bacteria, but not so high that they harm people.

Chlorine gas.

> **5** What is the state of chlorine at room temperature?
>
> **6** Is chlorine soluble in water? How can you tell?
>
> **7** What would be the problem with the water in a swimming pool if:
> a) not enough chlorine was added to the water
> b) too much chlorine was added to the water?
>
> **8** Draw a table like this in your book.

Properties of metals	Properties of non-metals

Using the information on the last four pages, and any other ideas that you have, complete the table to show the properties of metals and non-metals.

In the First World War chlorine was used as a poison gas. It was denser than air and filled up the trenches, killing many soldiers.

You should know...
● **Most non-metals are solids or gases.**
● **Non-metals do not conduct heat or electricity.**
● **Most non-metals have low melting and boiling points.**

What happens when elements combine?

All of the things in our world are made from the chemical elements. All the things in the picture, including the person, are made from just a few different elements. The elements join together to form **compounds**.

The millions of compounds in the natural world can be made from about 100 elements joined together in different ways. Chemists have managed to invent new products like dyes, detergents and plastics by finding new ways to get elements to react together.

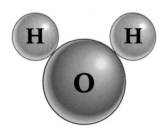

Water is a compound made from two elements: hydrogen and oxygen. The smallest particle of water contains two atoms of hydrogen and one atom of oxygen. This is called a **molecule** of water. We can show the number of atoms in a molecule by using the **chemical formula**. The chemical formula of water is H_2O.

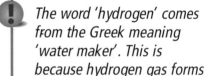

The word 'hydrogen' comes from the Greek meaning 'water maker'. This is because hydrogen gas forms water when it burns.

The hydrogen in this airship caught fire and reacted with the oxygen in the air causing a tragic disaster. Balloons and airships today use helium, which does not react with any other element.

1 Are each of the following elements or compounds?
   a) hydrogen   b) oxygen   c) water

2 a) How many elements are there in water?
   b) Write a word equation for a reaction in which water is formed.

3 Carbon dioxide has the formula CO_2 (the 'di-' in front of 'oxide' means there are two oxygen atoms).
   a) How many different *elements* are there in carbon dioxide?
   b) What are they?
   c) How many *atoms* are there in a molecule of carbon dioxide?
   d) Draw a diagram of a molecule of carbon dioxide.

Sulphur burns in oxygen. Heat is needed to start the reaction off. This heat energy turns some of the molecules of sulphur into individual atoms. The atoms of sulphur can then react with the oxygen to make the gas sulphur dioxide. We can show what happens in a chemical reaction using words or symbols. The **symbol equation** for this reaction is:

$$S + O_2 \longrightarrow SO_2$$

4 Write the word equation for the reaction that takes place when sulphur burns.

5 What is the chemical formula for a molecule of:
a) sulphur dioxide
b) oxygen?

6 Sulphur also forms a compound called sulphur trioxide.
a) What is the meaning of the prefix 'tri-' (e.g. in tripod or triangle)?
b) Write down the chemical formula for a molecule of sulphur trioxide.

Glucose is a more complicated molecule. It is made of three chemical elements joined together. The model below shows the way that carbon (black), hydrogen (white) and oxygen (red) atoms are joined together in a molecule of glucose.

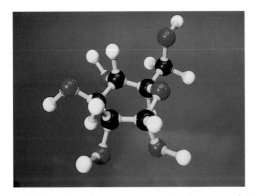

7 a) What is the total number of atoms in a molecule of glucose?
b) Write the chemical formula for glucose.

8 The chemical symbols Co and CO are very similar.
a) Which is a symbol that represents an atom of an element?
b) What is the name of the element?
c) Which is a chemical formula that represents a molecule of a compound?

This photograph shows James Watson (born 1928) and Francis Crick (born 1916) with their model of one of the most complicated molecules of all – DNA. They worked out the structure in 1952, allowing scientists to explain how parents pass on inherited information to their children.

P How could you carry out some tests on this green powder to try to find out whether it is an element or a compound?

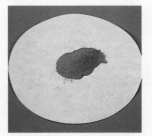

You should know...

- Elements can join together to make compounds.
- The name of a compound often tells you the elements that are in it.
- The smallest particle of many compounds is called a molecule.
- What a chemical formula is.

How can we represent the changes when new materials are made?

Many compounds are formed from just two elements. Common salt is an example. Sodium is a soft grey metal. Chlorine is a greenish-yellow gas. Both of these elements are dangerous. When sodium burns in chlorine a compound is made that is safe to eat – common salt. The chemical name for common salt is **sodium chloride**.

The chemical name tells us that it is made from sodium and chlorine. The '-**ide**' ending tells us that the elements have joined to make a compound. There are different ways we can show what happens. In each case, we show what we start with (the **reactants**) and what we end up with (the **products**). The symbol equation tells us that two atoms of sodium react with each molecule of chlorine gas to form a compound which has an equal number of sodium and chlorine atoms.

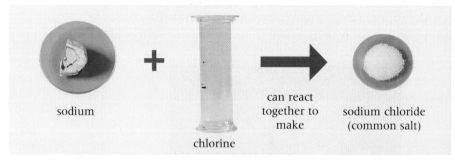

sodium + chlorine + can react together to make → sodium chloride (common salt)

A word equation: **sodium + chlorine ⟶ sodium chloride**

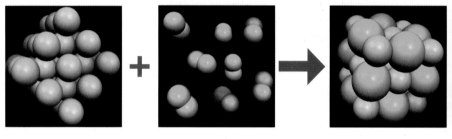

A symbol equation: **2Na + Cl$_2$ ⟶ 2NaCl**

 1 Write word and symbol equations to show what happens when these compounds are made:
a) carbon dioxide
b) water
c) sulphur trioxide.
(*Hint:* You may need to look back at pages 64 and 65.)

 2 When sodium chloride is made, what are:
a) the reactants   b) the products?

Magnesium burns with a bright flame to form a white ash. How would you find out whether the ash has a mass that is more or less than the magnesium that you started with?
● Make a prediction and explain your reasoning.
● Design an experiment to test your prediction.
● How would you make your experiment a fair test?

You should know...
● **How to represent chemical changes by word and symbol equations.**

Using electrolysis

How can we use electricity to split up compounds?

Electricity can be used to split up compounds into elements using a process called **electrolysis**. This photograph shows how electrolysis can be used on a large scale. This is a factory where aluminium is made. Aluminium oxide is found in a type of rock called **bauxite**. Bauxite is purified to get rid of rock debris. The aluminium oxide is then dissolved in molten cryolite, which is at 1500 °C. An electric current is passed through the molten cryolite and dissolved aluminium oxide to split it up like this:

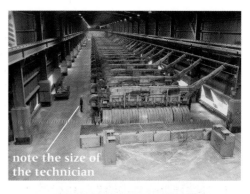
note the size of the technician

$$\text{aluminium oxide} \longrightarrow \text{aluminium + oxygen}$$

Enormous currents (up to 100 000 amps) are used in these factories.

 Electricity is used to deposit a thin layer of gold on the plugs of headphones. This reduces the electrical resistance of the contact and supposedly improves the sound quality. The layer of metal used in electroplating is about 0.001 mm thick!

In this example water is being split up by electrolysis into hydrogen and oxygen. The hydrogen from electrolysis can be used as a fuel. In the future, hydrogen may replace petrol as a fuel for cars.

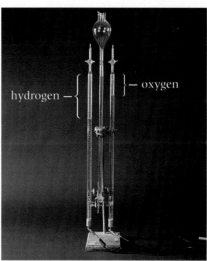
hydrogen — oxygen

 A fuel cell uses hydrogen and oxygen to produce electricity. The first hydrogen/oxygen fuel cell was invented by William Grove (1811–1895) in 1839. Today fuel cells are used to produce electricity on the Space Shuttle. They are also used in some cars and vans.

A hydrogen-powered van.

1 In aluminium factories, giant carbon blocks are used to carry the current. These can react with the oxygen that is given off to make another gas.
   a) Which gas do you think is formed?
   b) Write a word equation for the reaction.

2 a) Write a word equation for the reaction in which water is split up.
   b) Look at the photograph of this reaction above. The formula of water is H_2O. This means that each water molecule has two hydrogen atoms and one oxygen atom. How does the experiment provide some evidence to support this idea?

How are elements and compounds different?

pure hydrogen | pure oxygen | mixture of hydrogen and oxygen | compound of hydrogen and oxygen

This rocket uses liquid hydrogen as a fuel. Hydrogen is an **element** and so is made up of only hydrogen **atoms**. In the rocket the hydrogen is mixed with oxygen. Oxygen is also an element.

If you just mix the gases together nothing happens. To start the reaction a spark is needed. The spark causes the mixture of hydrogen and oxygen to explode. A chemical reaction takes place and a **compound** is formed. The hydrogen atoms and the oxygen atoms join together to make **molecules** of hydrogen oxide. Hydrogen oxide is much better known as water!

Since hydrogen and oxygen are elements, the atoms in each of their molecules are the same. For example, a hydrogen molecule contains two hydrogen atoms. We write the **chemical formula** of a hydrogen molecule as H_2. Water is a compound. It contains two different types of atom joined together: two hydrogen atoms and one oxygen atom. Its formula is written as H_2O.

1 What state (solid, liquid or gas) is:
   a) hydrogen
   b) oxygen
   c) the mixture of hydrogen and oxygen
   d) water?

2 Explain in your own words how water is different from the elements that make it up.

3 How do we write the formula for:
   a) an atom of hydrogen
   b) a molecule of hydrogen
   c) a molecule of water?

4 In a molecule of water:
   a) how many elements are there
   b) how many different atoms are there?

5 Molecules of sulphur have the formula S_8. The atoms are joined up in a ring.
   a) Draw a diagram of a molecule of sulphur.
   b) Is sulphur an element or a compound?
   c) How do you know?

Oxides are chemicals which contain oxygen joined to other types of atom. Carbon forms two different oxides. Carbon dioxide contains two oxygen atoms for every carbon atom ('di-' means two). Carbon dioxide is the gas that is produced by animals and plants during respiration. The other oxide only contains one oxygen atom. This is the deadly gas carbon monoxide ('mono-' means one).

carbon dioxide

carbon monoxide

Carbon monoxide can be produced by modern central heating boilers if they are not fitted properly and looked after. Carbon monoxide can kill. Some people have carbon monoxide alarms in their houses to warn them of the presence of this gas.

 6 a) What is the formula for carbon dioxide?
   b) Is carbon dioxide an element or a compound?
   c) How do you know?

7 Write down two other words that have 'mono' attached to them to mean one of something.

Most of the common substances around you are compounds. These diagrams show the atoms that make up three different acids.

hydrochloric acid

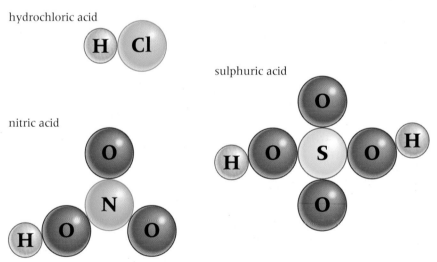

nitric acid

sulphuric acid

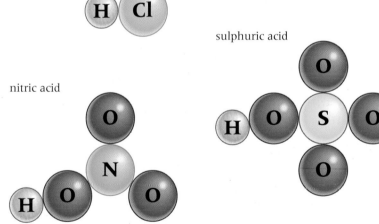

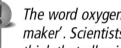 *The word oxygen means 'acid maker'. Scientists used to think that all acids contained oxygen. They were wrong!*

You should know...

- Elements contain only one kind of atom.

- Compounds contain more than one kind of atom joined together.

- A chemical formula tells you the number of each type of atom in a molecule.

 8 a) Which acid contains only two elements?
   b) Which acid contains five atoms in a molecule?

9 Which element is present in all three acids?

10 Write the chemical formula for each of the acids.

How do compounds differ from the elements from which they are made?

Iron and sulphur are both solid elements. Iron is magnetic, but sulphur is not. The photograph shows the elements in powder form. There is also a mixture of iron and sulphur. The elements in the mixture are not combined together. If you pass a magnet over the mixture, only the iron is attracted towards the magnet. The sulphur stays on the dish.

iron filings

sulphur powder

iron and sulphur

1 Describe the appearance of:
 a) the iron
 b) the sulphur
 c) the mixture of iron and sulphur.

2 Which of the elements is:
 a) a metal
 b) a non-metal?

3 How can you tell that the iron and sulphur do not form a compound when you just mix them together?

Iron and sulphur react together when you heat them. The atoms of iron and sulphur join together to form a compound called iron sulphide. Once the reaction has started, you can take the tube out of the flame, and it will carry on glowing. Energy is released when the atoms join (or **bond**) together and this energy is given out into the air.

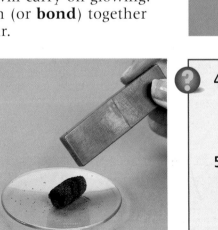

When the reaction is over, the iron and sulphur have bonded together to form a single solid substance. You cannot separate out the iron in iron sulphide using a magnet because it is bonded too strongly to the sulphur. The word equation is:

iron + sulphur ⟶ iron sulphide

4 From the word equation, write down the names of:
 a) a compound
 b) two elements.

5 Give one piece of evidence that suggests that iron sulphide is a different substance from:
 a) iron
 b) sulphur.

What other tests might you carry out to show that iron sulphide behaves differently from the elements that make it up?

Iron sulphide is a solid with the atoms arranged in a regular pattern. The atoms do not join together in simple molecules. The formula of iron sulphide is FeS. This means that for every iron atom in the solid there is one sulphur atom. The formula shows us that the ratio of iron atoms to sulphur atoms is 1:1.

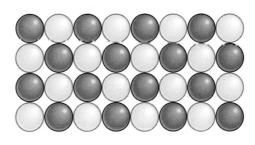

A particle diagram to show the arrangement of atoms in iron sulphide.

Limestone is mainly calcium carbonate and can be found in many different countries in the world. The formula of calcium carbonate is $CaCO_3$. This means that the calcium carbonate from this quarry in Germany will have exactly the same ratio of calcium, carbon and oxygen atoms as calcium carbonate that we find in the UK. A chemical compound always contains the same elements in the same ratio. If the ratio changes, it means that you have got a different chemical compound.

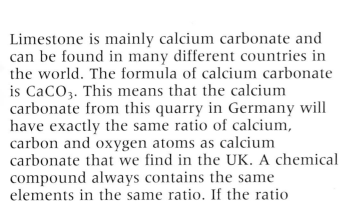

6 Magnesium oxide is a solid with the formula MgO. Draw a particle diagram to show the arrangement of the atoms in solid magnesium oxide. Show at least 12 atoms.

7 a) What is the ratio of calcium, carbon and oxygen in calcium carbonate?

  b) If all the three types of atoms had an equal mass, what would be the percentage of each of the elements in calcium carbonate?

  c) The actual percentages are: 40% calcium, 12% carbon and 48% oxygen. Based on the actual percentages, which of the three different atoms is heaviest? Explain your answer.

You should know...

● Compounds contain elements that are chemically combined.

● The properties of a compound are different from those of the elements that make it up.

● A compound always contains the same proportions of each element.

Which substances react just by mixing?

Iron metal reacts with the copper sulphate solution as soon as they are mixed together. In this picture, the iron has reacted with the copper sulphate solution, and solid copper has been formed. You can see it as a coating on the nails. Two new substances (the **products**) have been formed.

The word equation for this reaction is:

iron + **copper sulphate** ⟶ **iron sulphate** + **copper**

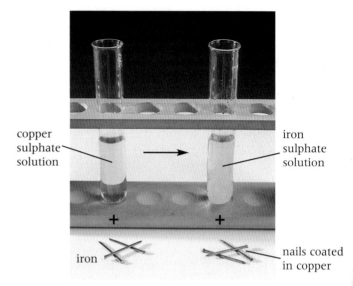

copper sulphate solution → iron sulphate solution

iron

nails coated in copper

Here is an example of a reaction between two liquids.

 1 How can you tell that iron reacts with the copper sulphate solution? (*Hint*: There are two things that you can see.)

When the solutions in the two tubes on the left are mixed, we can see that a reaction takes place. There is a colour change. A new, solid substance is formed by mixing the two liquids. An insoluble solid that is formed in this way is called a **precipitate**.

You can also tell that a reaction is taking place if:

- bubbles of gas form or
- the temperature changes.

 2 Look at the photograph above. How can you tell that a reaction has taken place?

3 What state is the dark blue substance in:
a) tube A   b) tube C?

4 How could you separate the dark blue substance in tube C from the liquid?

5 What do the following words mean?
a) precipitate   b) reactants   c) products

You should know...

- In a chemical reaction, reactants turn into products.

- When you make an insoluble solid from two substances in solutions, this is called a precipitate.

How can heat break up compounds?

Heating can make things change state. The heat from the hair dryer is being used to evaporate the water on the girl's hair and make it go into the air. This is a **physical** change. The water vapour can easily turn back into liquid water again. This is *not* a chemical reaction, as no new substance is being formed.

 1 Is evaporation a chemical reaction? Explain your answer.

Here the heat has been used to produce a chemical reaction. Bread contains starch. The bread has changed colour because the starch in it has been changed into carbon – the toast has burned and turned black. Although we can scrape the black bits off, we can't change them back into bread again. This is an **irreversible** change. A chemical reaction has taken place. The starch has **decomposed**. We can show this with a word equation:

$$\text{starch} \longrightarrow \text{carbon} + \text{water vapour}$$

When you mix chemicals together, or heat them, how can you tell if a chemical reaction has taken place?
- How will you record your observations?
- Which observations provide the best evidence?

 2 What are the two products formed when starch is changed by heat?

3 From the word equation, write down the names of:
a) one element
b) two compounds.

4 Is burning toast a chemical reaction? Explain your answer.

5 If the toast is set on fire so that it burns completely, a gas is formed instead of the black carbon. What is the name of this gas?

You should know...
- Some compounds can be split up using heat.

How are mixtures different from elements and compounds?

Different parts of the United Kingdom are known for their drinks. For example, whisky is made in some parts of Scotland and beer is brewed in the Midlands. So why isn't whisky made in Birmingham? The answer lies in the water.

The water used to make drinks is clean but it is not **pure** because it contains other chemicals apart from water. As the water flows over rocks, chemicals from them dissolve in it. Water from different areas contains different amounts of chemicals which makes it taste different. The different types of water are suitable for making different types of drink. The labels on mineral water bottles tell us what these other chemicals are.

	Volvic (mg/litre)	Highland Spring (mg/litre)	Malvern (mg/litre)
Calcium	10	35	35
Magnesium	6	9	15
Sodium	9	6	15
Potassium	6	1	1
Bicarbonate	65	136	123
Chloride	8	8	39
Sulphate	7	6	35
Nitrate	6	0	8

Different substances found in mineral waters.

 1 Look at the table on the left. Which water contains the greatest mass of chemicals?

2 What do we mean by 'pure water'?

The water that we drink is a **mixture** of water and other chemicals. Water is a compound and the other chemicals dissolved in it are also compounds. So mineral water is a mixture of compounds. There are many other sorts of mixtures.

 3 Name two other mixtures, apart from those on this page.

Sulphur and iron – a mixture of two solid elements.

Sea water – a mixture of water, common salt and other soluble compounds dissolved in the water.

Muddy water – a mixture of insoluble solid compounds and a liquid compound.

Rock – a mixture of solid compounds.

Shaving foam – a mixture of a liquid compound and a compound which is a gas.

Air – a mixture of compounds and elements which are all gases.

4 Draw a table with three columns headed element, compound and mixture. Put these substances into the correct column of your table.

carbon dioxide   common salt   ink
iron   magnesium oxide   nitrogen
oxygen   plastic   rock   soil

The compounds or elements in a mixture do not join up with one another, they are simply jumbled up together. We can represent compounds and elements by formulae but we cannot use formulae for mixtures. This is because the amounts of all the different chemicals in a mixture can change. For example, air is a mixture of gases. Breathed out air contains more carbon dioxide than breathed in air. Warm air can contain more water vapour than cold air.

In ancient times it was believed that both air and water were elements. In 1674, John Mayow (1640–1679) did some experiments which showed that a part of the air was used up when a candle burnt in it. His experiments showed that air therefore contained at least two gases. Antoine Lavoisier (1743–1794) provided more evidence for this and came to the conclusion that air is a mixture. Lavoisier also showed that water is a compound of hydrogen and oxygen.

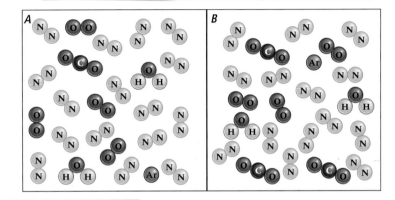

5 Give the name of a gas in the air which:
 a) exists as single atoms (*Hint*: You might need to look at the Periodic Table on page 158.)
 b) is made out of molecules which contain three atoms
 c) is an element with more than one atom in a molecule
 d) is a compound.

6 Look at the two drawings of the particles in air. Which drawing shows breathed out air?

7 There is no formula for mineral water. Why not?

Natural gas is used to cook with and heat our homes. It is mostly methane but it also contains some other gases. The chemical formula for methane is CH_4.

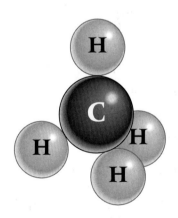

8 Is natural gas pure methane? Explain your answer.

9 Is methane an element, a mixture or a compound? Explain your answer.

10 In a molecule of methane:
 a) how many atoms are there
 b) how many elements are there?

You should know...
- The difference between a mixture and a compound.
- What a pure substance is.

How can we tell if something is pure?

Orange juice is often described as **pure** because it has no added ingredients. All the juice has come straight from oranges.

1 Explain why:
   a) supermarkets would describe the orange juice as pure
   b) scientists would describe the orange juice as a mixture.

Scientists say that orange juice is a mixture because it contains many different chemicals, and not just one.
A pure element contains only one type of atom.
A compound is pure if it only contains one substance with a definite chemical formula.

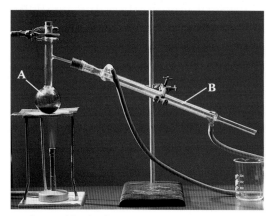

A still is used for distillation.

We can often tell if something is pure or a mixture of substances by trying to separate out the different substances. For example, the dissolved solid colours in black ink can be easily separated using **chromatography**. We can separate the water from black ink using **distillation**.

Chromatograms of two black inks.

2 a) How many different colours make up the black ink used in the chromatograms?
   b) A type of ink only contains one dye. How would you obtain a pure sample of this dye without using chromatography?

3 Distillation is evaporation followed by condensation. Look at the photograph above of the apparatus used for distilling.
   a) In which part of the apparatus (A or B) does condensation occur?
   b) What is the whole of the apparatus used in distillation called?
   c) What liquid will collect in the beaker if the ink is heated?
   d) Will this liquid be pure? Explain your answer.

4 Solid carbon dioxide ('dry ice') is used to make the 'smoke' seen on TV and in the theatre. Suggest a use for pure oxygen.

Air can be separated by using the fact that the different gases have different boiling points. If you cool air down to −79 °C carbon dioxide becomes a solid which can easily be collected. A type of distillation is used to separate the other gases from liquid air, which has been cooled to −200 °C.

You should know...
- Mixtures can often be separated easily.

How is air separated?

Air is made of a number of different gases as shown in the pie chart.

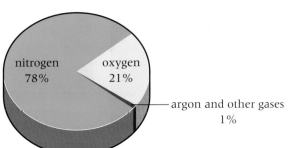

We can separate these gases from liquid air using **fractional distillation**. The main gases that are separated are nitrogen, oxygen and argon. First, the carbon dioxide, water vapour and dust are removed from the air. These substances clog up the apparatus used to make liquid air. The air is then compressed, cooled and allowed to expand. When the air expands it gets even cooler. This is repeated a few times and eventually it becomes a liquid.

> **!** *You can show that air cools as it expands by holding a thermometer next to a deflating bicycle tyre.*

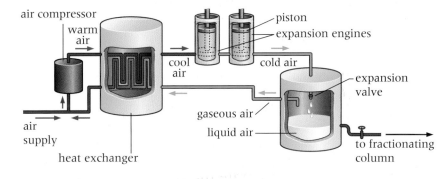

The liquid air is then pumped into a **fractionating column**, a huge tower, several storeys high. Nitrogen has a boiling point of −195 °C, argon boils at −185 °C and oxygen boils at −182 °C. The liquid air is warmed to −185 °C. The nitrogen and argon boil off and the gases are collected at the top of the tower. The liquid is now richer in oxygen and the process is repeated until all the nitrogen and argon have boiled away and you end up with pure liquid oxygen.

A fractionating column.

1 a) Name one way of removing carbon dioxide from a sample of air in the laboratory.
   b) Why would carbon dioxide block up the cooling apparatus?

2 If you used a temperature of −195 °C at the bottom of the fractionating column, the nitrogen collected at the top would still not be pure.
   a) Explain why not.
   b) Suggest how you could make it purer.

3 Suggest how pure argon is made.

4 Find out:
   a) the names of two other gases found in air and their boiling points.
   b) two uses each for nitrogen, oxygen and argon.

How can melting and boiling points help to tell us if something is pure?

The temperature at which a solid changes into a liquid is called its **melting point**. When a liquid changes into a gas it is said to **evaporate**. The temperature at which evaporation happens most quickly is called the **boiling point**. At this temperature the liquid can get no hotter (although the gas can).

Iron melts at 1535 °C . It boils at 2750 °C.

Stearic acid is a type of wax, which has a melting point of 69 °C. It is found in candle wax.

Sulphur melts at 112 °C and boils at 444 °C.

Sodium melts at 97 °C. It boils at 882 °C.

Gallium is a metal which will melt in your hand. It melts at 29 °C.

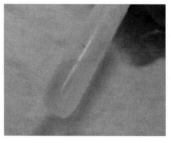
This is liquid oxygen! It melts at −218 °C and boils at −182 °C.

Tungsten will not melt until it reaches 3410 °C.

1 What is the melting point of tungsten?

2 At what temperature will liquid sodium evaporate as fast as it can?

3 Name one liquid that would boil in a kitchen freezer.

4 Do you think that boiling points are always higher than melting points? Explain your reasoning.

P How would you find out if adding salt to water changes its boiling point?
- Does it matter how much salt you use?
- How would you make sure your results are fair and reliable?

The melting point of a substance is also its **freezing point**. At precisely 0 °C *pure* water will be an equal mixture of water and ice. Slightly above this temperature and all the ice will become liquid, slightly below it and all the liquid water will become ice.

5 What is the freezing point of:
a) iron
b) oxygen
c) sodium?

Pure elements and pure compounds have precise melting and boiling points. Mixtures do not. They melt and boil over a range of temperatures.

Pure water melts and boils at 100 °C. Impurities in the water can change the melting and boiling points. Adding salt to water lowers its melting point which is why salt is spread on the roads in winter. Adding sugar to water makes the melting point lower and the boiling point higher.

Solder is a mixture of tin and lead. Both these metals melt quite easily but the mixture of tin and lead melts at a lower temperature than either of the two metals when they are pure.

8 Why is salt spread on the roads in winter?

9 Why do ice lollies need to be kept well below the freezing point of water?

10 How do you think antifreeze affects the freezing point of water?

11 Pure ethanol (alcohol) has a boiling point of 78 °C. White wines often contain 10% ethanol. Almost all the rest of the wine is water.
   a) Approximately what percentage of the wine is water?
   b) Estimate the boiling point of white wine. Explain your reasoning.

6 Two types of wax were melted. Wax A melted at exactly 69 °C. Wax B melted between 61 °C and 69 °C. Which type of wax was a pure substance? Explain your answer.

7 Chemistry data books list the melting and boiling points of many substances. However, the melting and boiling points of air are never given. Why not?

In 1714 Gabriel Fahrenheit (1686–1736), a German scientist, built a thermometer. He needed a scale to put on the thermometer. He mixed ice with different types of salt. The salts lowered the freezing point, but some worked better than others. He decided that the temperature of the coldest mixture that he could make should be zero degrees on his scale. Zero degrees on the Fahrenheit scale is about –18 °C.

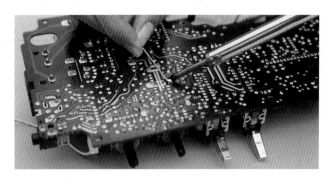

Soldering is used to join metals together.

You should know...

● **For any substance, the freezing point and the melting point are the same.**

● **Pure substances have precise melting and boiling points.**

● **Impurities change the melting and boiling points.**

● **Mixtures melt and boil over a range of temperatures.**

How can we describe rocks?

There are many different types of rock. Rocks are made of different **grains** which fit together. Each grain is made of a chemical compound, called a **mineral**. Rocks are **mixtures** of different minerals.

 1 What is a mineral?

2 What is a grain?

The grains in rocks can be different sizes and shapes. The combination of sizes and shapes of grains is called the **texture** of the rock. In some rocks the grains all fit together with no gaps. We say that the grains are **interlocking**. Interlocking grains are sometimes called **crystals**. Rocks made of interlocking grains are usually hard.

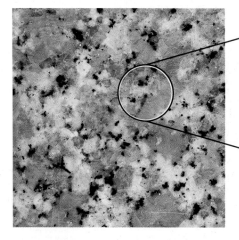
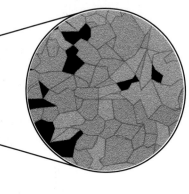

Granite has interlocking grains.

In other rocks the grains are more rounded, and there are gaps between them. Rocks like this are not usually as strong as rocks made from interlocking crystals. Rocks made of rounded grains can absorb water because water can get into the gaps between the grains. The rocks are said to be **porous**.

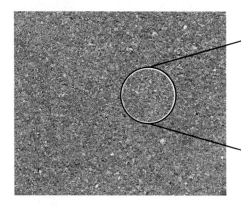
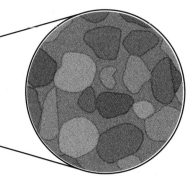

Sandstone has rounded grains.

 3 Look carefully at the photographs on this page. Write down the name of a rock that has:
   a) rounded grains
   b) interlocking grains.

4 Why do rocks made from rounded grains absorb water?

How could you investigate whether some rocks are more porous than others?
- How would you carry out a fair test?

Geological maps show where different types of rock are found. The first geological map was drawn by Christopher Packe (1686–1749) in 1743. It showed the rocks in Kent.

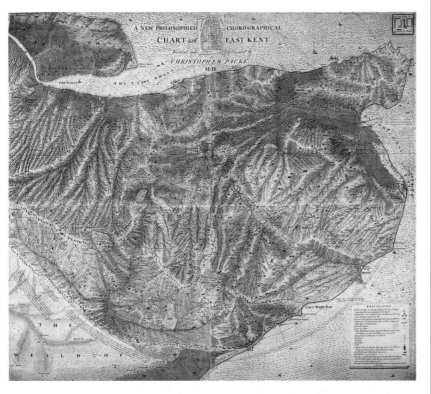

Rocks are transparent if you slice them thinly enough! Geologists use microscopes to look at thin sections of rocks to learn about the minerals in them.

A thin section of granite seen through a microscope.

5 A piece of rock is hard, and does not absorb water. What can you say about the texture of this rock?

6 Write down three ways in which granite is different from sandstone.

You should know...

- Rocks are made up of mixtures of minerals.
- The grains in rock can be interlocking or rounded.
- The texture of a rock depends on the size and shape of the grains.
- Rocks with rounded grains are often porous.

Why does the shape of rocks change?

These statues are both on the outside of Westminster Abbey in London. The statue on the left is new. The one on the right is hundreds of years old. Parts of the statue have been worn away, mainly by rain. We say the statue has been **weathered**.

Rain is slightly acidic because it contains dissolved gases from the air which make it acidic. When the rain falls onto rocks it can react with the minerals in the rock. This is called **chemical weathering**.

> **1** Why is rain acidic?
>
> **2** What happens when rain falls onto rocks?

Some rocks are weathered faster than others. Limestone and chalk are weathered very easily by the acidic rain.

The gaps in this 'limestone pavement' were formed when acidic rainwater reacted with the limestone. The new materials formed in the reaction dissolved and were carried away when the water ran off the rock. It took thousands of years for these gaps to form.

Granite is weathered much more slowly than limestone. The acid in the rain reacts with the minerals and gradually changes them. The new minerals formed are weaker than the original minerals. The new minerals can crumble and get washed away. Eventually enough minerals have been washed away to make the granite weak and crumbly.

Weathered granite.

Unweathered granite.

> **3** Does granite or limestone react faster with rain?
>
> **4** Why does chemical weathering form gaps in limestone?
>
> **5** What happens to the minerals in granite when it is weathered?

You should know...
- Rain is naturally acidic.
- Chemical weathering happens when rocks react with rainwater.

Limestone caves

How are limestone caves formed?

Caves are often found in limestone areas. Rainwater falling on limestone slowly finds its way down through tiny cracks in the rock. Limestone is made of a chemical called calcium carbonate, which reacts slightly with acidic rainwater. The salts formed in the reaction are soluble and get washed away. Over thousands of years enough limestone reacts to form caves.

Sometimes the roof of a cave collapses. The broken pieces of rock dissolve faster than the solid rock did. The dissolved calcium carbonate is carried away by the water flowing through the cave.

Many limestone caves have stalactites and stalagmites. Rain containing dissolved calcium carbonate drips through cracks in the roof of the cave. If the water evaporates, some of the calcium carbonate **precipitates** and forms solid calcium carbonate again. More drips evaporate at the same place, each one depositing tiny amounts of calcium carbonate. Eventually a stalactite forms, hanging down from the roof.

Many caves have water running through them.

Drips running down the stalactite fall onto the floor of the cave and evaporate, and a little more calcium carbonate is deposited each time. A stalagmite gradually forms beneath the stalactite.

?
1 What is limestone made from?

2 Why do caves often form in limestone?

3 Try to explain why fallen pieces of rock dissolve faster than the solid rock did.

4 Draw a labelled diagram to explain how stalactites and stalagmites form.

How do changes in temperature cause rocks to weather?

Rocks can be weathered by **physical changes**. When it is hot, the minerals in rocks **expand** (get bigger). When they cool, they **contract** (get smaller). These changes in size produce strong forces between the minerals. If the rock is heated and cooled over and over again, the forces can make cracks. This kind of **physical weathering** often causes sheets of rock to peel off.

Weathering caused by repeated heating and cooling.

 1 What makes the minerals in a rock expand?

2 What can make cracks form in rocks?

Changes in temperature have an even greater effect if water gets trapped in cracks in the rock. When the water gets cold enough it freezes and expands, forcing the rock apart. When the temperature rises the water melts and runs further into the crack. If this water freezes again, the crack will get even bigger. This is called **freeze-thaw** action.

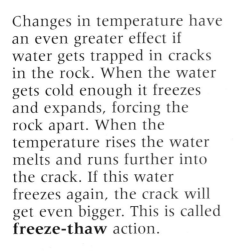

Water freezing inside this jar has expanded and split it apart.

These cracks in the rock face were widened by freeze-thaw action which also caused the rock fragments to break off.

 3 a) What happens to water when it freezes?
b) How can this cause physical weathering?

Plants can also break up rocks. Their roots can grow into cracks in the rocks. When the roots grow bigger they make the crack wider and the rock can break apart.

 4 How can plants break rocks apart?

Bits of rock loosened by weathering may fall from the rock face. This changes the shape of the rock. This movement of bits of rock is called **erosion**.

The bits of rock at the bottom of the mountain were broken off by physical weathering.

P A sculptor wants to carve a stone statue that will last for a long time. How would you investigate which is the best rock to use?

 Mountaineers try to climb early in the day before the heat of the Sun warms the rocks. Loose bits of rock are held up by ice, and when the ice melts, rocks and stones start to fall.

 5 Why are rock fragments often found at the bottom of cliffs?

6 Would you expect freeze-thaw action to happen in the following places? Explain your answers.
   a) Scotland, where it rains a lot and it gets very cold in the winter.
   b) The Sahara Desert, where it is very hot in the day time and gets cold at night, but it hardly ever rains.
   c) The Antarctic, where it is very cold all the time.

You should know...

● Rocks can be physically weathered by changes in temperature.

● Water expands when it freezes.

● Water freezing in cracks in rocks can widen the cracks. This is called freeze-thaw action.

What happens to weathered pieces of rock?

Rock fragments fall to the bottom of rock faces. If they fall into a stream or river, they can get **transported** (carried away). As they are transported by the water, the rock fragments knock against each other and wear away. This is called **abrasion**. The bits of rock in a stream or river are called **sediment**.

These rocks have been worn away and rounded by abrasion while they were carried along in the river.

> **?**
> 1 How do rock fragments get worn away in streams and rivers?
>
> 2 a) What happens to the shape of rocks that are transported in streams?
>   b) What do you think happens to their masses? Explain your answer.
>
> 3 What is sediment?

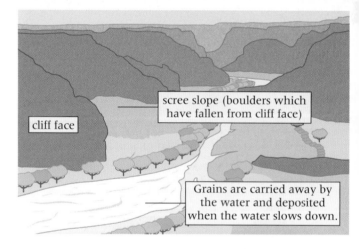

cliff face

scree slope (boulders which have fallen from cliff face)

Grains are carried away by the water and deposited when the water slows down.

If water is moving fast it can move quite large pieces of rock. These rocks were carried down the river bed by a 'flash flood', when there was a lot of very fast-moving water.

When a river flows into a lake or the sea it slows down. The slow-moving water cannot carry all of the sediment, and so it **deposits** (drops) it on the bottom. The photographs below show how this happens.

The water in this jar has just been swirled.

The water in the jar has stopped moving.

P. How would you find out how far water can carry grains of rock? What would happen if you changed these things:
- the flow of water
- the width of the stream
- the size of the grains of rock?

 The Mississippi river carries 550 million tonnes of sediment each year, which it deposits when it flows into the Gulf of Mexico. The sediment from the river builds the coast outwards by about 90 m each year.

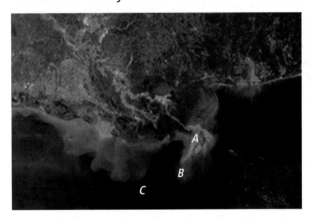

? **4** Why does the sand get deposited at the bottom of the jar in the right-hand picture?

5 After a rain storm, rivers often have a lot of fast-flowing water in them.
a) Why do flooded rivers usually look dirty?
b) Where has the dirt come from?
c) What happens when the water level drops?

6 Look at the photograph of the Mississippi river.
a) Would you expect large pebbles to be deposited at A, B or C? Explain your answer.
b) Which way is the current flowing in the Gulf of Mexico? Explain your answer.

7 You can show what happens when rocks are carried by water by shaking some sugar cubes in a jar.
a) Explain what will happen when the jar is shaken.
b) Explain how this can demonstrate what happens to rocks carried by water.
c) In what ways is this not a good model for rocks in a stream?

You should know...
- Rock fragments can be transported by flowing water.
- Smaller rock fragments are carried further than large ones.
- Rock fragments get worn away while they are being transported.

Why do sediments form layers?

Sediments carried by rivers are deposited on the bottom of the river, or they are deposited on the sea bed when the river flows out to sea. Over thousands of years many deposited sediments turn into rock. Rocks formed from sediments often have layers.

1 What happens to the sediments carried by a river when it flows into the sea?

2 How might you be able to tell that a rock was formed from sediments?

Layers in rocks form because rivers do not always transport the same kinds of sediments. When the river is flowing slowly, it may only be able to carry mud or tiny pieces of sand. The layers of sediment deposited by the river will form rock with very small grains.

When the river flows fast it can carry larger pieces of rock. The sediments deposited will be larger, and will form rock with larger grains.

Most water contains dissolved chemicals called **salts**. When rivers flow over rocks, some of the chemicals in the rocks dissolve in the water. When the water evaporates the salts are left behind and can form layers.

3 Where does the salt in sea water come from?

4 How can you get the salt from sea water?

This rock was formed from very fine grains.

The rock fragments that formed this rock were carried by fast-flowing water.

ThrustSSC - the world's first supersonic car - was tested on Black Rock Desert, Nevada. The surface is very flat and smooth, because it is made of salt that was left behind when water in a lake evaporated.

A fossilised leaf in a lump of coal.

Dead plants and animals fall to the bottom of marshes, lakes and the sea. If they get covered by other sediments they do not rot away, but can form **fossils**. If a lot of plant material is buried at once in a marsh, it may turn into **coal**. When tiny plants in the sea get buried, they sometimes turn into **oil** or **natural gas** trapped under a layer of rock.

Limestone is a rock that is formed from fragments of the shells of sea creatures. Sometimes whole shells or other hard parts can be seen in the rock.

These pieces are the remains of small animals called crinoids, or sea lilies.

A fossil fish.

William Smith (1769–1839) was the first person to use fossils to identify the ages of layers of rock. He published his book in 1815.

!
Fossils show that the whole of southern England was once covered in a warm sea. It was about as warm as the Mediterranean is today!

Scientists think that crinoids looked like this when they were alive.

5 What are fossils?

6 Why does limestone often contain lots of fossils?

You should know...

- Sediments often form layers.
- Some layers of sediment are formed when water evaporates and leaves salts behind.
- Parts of dead plants or animals can sometimes be preserved as fossils.

What can fossils tell us?

Fossils can show us what some living things looked like in the past.

Scientists can learn a lot from fossils like the shells of **extinct** sea creatures, or from microscopic fossils, such as pollen grains or tiny animals. Larger fossils can sometimes be found, and Mary Anning was one of the first people to find skeletons of extinct animals that were almost complete.

The Annings were a poor family who lived in Lyme Regis in Dorset. Mary's father died when she was only 10, and the rest of the family managed to make some money from selling fossils they had collected. Mary took over the fossil-selling business and made several important finds, including the first skeletons of *Ichthyosaurus*, *Plesiosaurus* and *Pterodactyl*.

Mary Anning (1799–1847).

Mary and her family discovered the first specimen of Ichthyosaurus.

Pleisiosaurus.

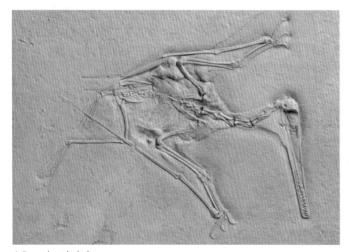
A Pterodactyl *skeleton.*

1 What can fossils tell us about the past?

2 Look at the skeleton of the *Ichthyosaurus*.
   a) Did the animal live in the sea or on land? Explain your answer.
   b) Where do you think the animal was in its food chain? Explain your answer.

3 Small fossils like sea shells are much more common than large ones like *Ichthyosaurus* skeletons. Why do you think this is?

4 Fossils of sea creatures are much more common than fossils of creatures that lived on land. Why do you think this is?

5 Find out more about Mary Anning and her life.

How is soil formed?

Soil is a very important part of the Earth. Most plants need soil to grow in. Soil is a mixture of stones (bits of broken rock), smaller rock particles, and **humus** (the remains of dead plants and animals).

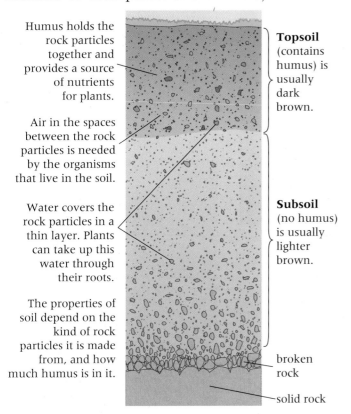

Humus holds the rock particles together and provides a source of nutrients for plants.

Air in the spaces between the rock particles is needed by the organisms that live in the soil.

Water covers the rock particles in a thin layer. Plants can take up this water through their roots.

The properties of soil depend on the kind of rock particles it is made from, and how much humus is in it.

Topsoil (contains humus) is usually dark brown.

Subsoil (no humus) is usually lighter brown.

broken rock

solid rock

Soil profile – the deeper you dig, the bigger the particles get, until you reach solid rock.

Clay soil.

Sandy soil.

Clay soils	Sandy soils
very small particles	larger particles
hold water, as it cannot drain away easily between the particles	water drains easily through the gaps between the particles
'heavy', and difficult to dig when wet	easy to dig
not much air	plenty of air

A comparison of clay and sandy soils.

The 'best' soil for growing plants contains humus and both clay and sand particles. This type of soil is called **loam**.

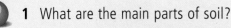

1 What are the main parts of soil?

2 Why does a sandy soil contain more air than a clay soil?

3 Think about the differences between a clay soil and a sandy soil.
   a) Which type of soil will contain the most organisms? Explain your answer.
   b) Which is most likely to flood if it rains a lot? Explain your answer.
   c) Which soil would keep plants alive longer in a drought? Explain your answer.

Manure tea – made by adding manure to water and leaving it for a day – can be used to give plants extra nutrients just before they start to flower. The tea should be put onto the ground around the plant and washed into the ground with water.

How are sedimentary rocks formed?

Each of these rocks is made up of **grains** which fit together. Different grains are made out of different **minerals** and each type of rock has a mixture of different grains. These rocks have been **weathered** by physical and chemical processes.

1 Look at photographs A, B and C carefully. What has caused the weathering shown in each photograph?

2 Which photographs show examples of:
a) physical weathering   b) chemical weathering?
c) Explain your reasoning.

3 If a piece of rock has been weathered by a biological process, what would you expect to see in a photograph of it?

The bottom of this slow-moving stream is covered in a layer of sediment made up of very small particles.

When rock is weathered, pieces may fall from the rock face. These fragments of rock can be carried away (**transported**) by moving water. This is called **erosion**. The amount of rock and the size of the rock fragments that can be carried depends on how fast the water is flowing. Slow-moving water can only carry tiny fragments of rock. Fast-moving water can carry much larger fragments. When the water flows too slowly to carry the fragments any more, they sink and are said to be **deposited**. The deposited rock fragments form a layer of **sediment**.

Over a long period of time, more layers of sediment are deposited on top of the first one. As this happens, the newer layers on top squash the bottom layers.

Different layers of sediment can be different colours and have different textures depending on the type of fragments deposited.

The pressure from these newer layers forces the grains of sediment closer together. This squashing (called **compaction**) squeezes the water out from between the grains. This can be shown by squeezing wet sand.

When wet grains of sand are squashed together, water runs out and the grains of sand stick together.

 Sand and sandstone are both made of the same material. How would you find out how the grains of each substance are held together?
Look at some other samples of sedimentary rocks (e.g. conglomerate, limestone, mudstone).
- What do they have in common?
- What are the characteristics of these rocks?

The grains of sediments have gaps between them. Water can flow through these gaps. If the water contains dissolved minerals, the minerals can crystallise in the gaps as a 'glue' that **cements** the grains together. **Compaction** and **cementation** together change sediments into sedimentary rocks.

Sedimentary rocks are mixtures of minerals, and some contain **fossils** as well. Many sedimentary rocks have gaps between the grains. Rocks like this can contain water and are said to be **porous**.

Sandstone.

Chalk.

Limestone.

Shale.

These rocks are all different sedimentary rocks. Although they are very different, they were all formed when layers of sediment were compacted and cemented together.

4 How is sedimentary rock made from a layer of sediment?

5 Would the oldest sedimentary rocks be at the top or the bottom of a cliff? Explain your answer.

6 Where does the glue come from that holds the grains together in a sedimentary rock?

7 What are the characteristics of sedimentary rocks?

You should know...
- **Different sediments contain fragments of different sizes.**
- **Layers of sediment form sedimentary rock when they are compacted (squeezed) and cemented (glued) together.**
- **Sedimentary rocks have grainy textures, may be porous and may contain fossils.**

Are all limestones different?

As soon as plants and animals die, they start to rot away. However, sometimes parts of the plants and animals are turned into rock and form **fossils**.

Fossilised remains of a plant in shale.

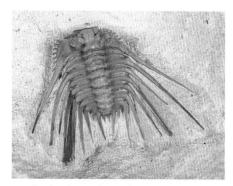

Fossilised remains of a trilobite in limestone.

Fossils form when dead plants or animals become covered in a layer of sediment which protects them. Over millions of years, more layers of sediment may be deposited. The upper layers of sediment squash the lower layers, which turn into sedimentary rock. The parts of the animals and plants in the lower layers also turn into rock but keep their shapes.

The fossil of a large animal being uncovered.

1 What are fossils?

2 Sediment protects the bones of dead animals from being moved. How else do you think the sediment protects the bones?

3 Name one place where you think a dead plant or animal is likely to become a fossil. Explain your reasoning.

 Fossils found in the Alps show that these mountains were once part of an ancient sea bed.

Sometimes a layer of sediment will be made of broken up bits of shell. This can often happen in the sea, when creatures with shells die on the sea bed. Many of the shells get broken by the moving water. If these layers of shell are covered with other layers of sediment they can turn into **limestone**.

4 The limestones below are all different. Describe the differences in their appearance.

5 Why do different sorts of limestone have different colours?

Limestone is an example of a **carbonate-rich** rock since it is mainly made of a white mineral called calcium carbonate. However, other minerals may also be present in the rock (formed, for example, from sand or mud mixed with the shells) and so limestones come in different colours.

Fossilferous limestone. Chalk. Yellow limestone.

P Carbonates react with acid to form a salt, carbon dioxide gas and water. For example:

calcium + **hydrochloric** ⟶ **calcium** + **carbon** + **water**
carbonate　　**acid**　　　　　　**chloride**　　**dioxide**

How would you find out how much calcium carbonate is found in two different sorts of limestone?
● How could you make sure your test is fair?

All limestones contain calcium carbonate, but the limestone may have been formed in different ways. Like most limestones, **chalk** was formed from the remains of microscopic organisms. These remains collected at the bottom of shallow lagoons. The rocks are white because they do not contain many impurities.

Chalk is formed from the remains of microscopic organisms.

Coquina is formed from larger fragments of shell and coral.

Calcium carbonate is slightly soluble in water. Some limestones are formed when this calcium carbonate is left behind after some of the water has evaporated. **Oolite** is an example of a limestone which was formed in this way. The calcium carbonate formed a precipitate on the beds of tropical seas and lagoons as high temperatures caused the sea water to evaporate.

! *Items that can absorb water are hung up in the Petrifying Well at Old Mother Shipton's Cave in Knaresborough, North Yorkshire. The water evaporates and leaves behind calcium carbonate which turns the items into limestone!*

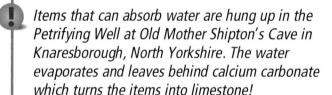

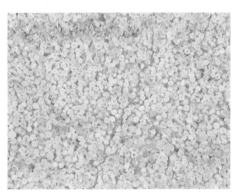

Oolite was formed from calcium carbonate precipitated when sea water evaporated.

? 6 What do all limestones have in common?

7 Describe two ways in which limestone can be formed.

8 Why is the percentage of calcium carbonate in oolite likely to be higher than in limestone formed in a muddy pool?

9 Find out how coral reefs can be turned into limestone.

You should know...

● All limestones are mainly calcium carbonate but may contain other minerals depending on where and how they were formed.

How are metamorphic rocks formed?

Rocks are made up of different minerals. When the minerals are heated and compressed (squashed), they can change into different ones. **Metamorphic** means 'changed', so rocks that are formed by changing one rock into another are called **metamorphic rocks**.

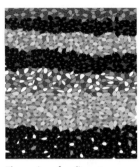

The grains of sedimentary rocks are usually deposited in layers called beds.

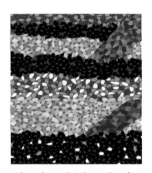

When the rock is heated and compressed new layers start to form. These are often in a different direction.

Sometimes the heat and pressure causes new minerals to form. Metamorphic rocks often have crystals in layers.

 1 What does metamorphic mean?

Over a long time layers of sedimentary rock build up on the sea bed. After these rocks are formed, they may get compressed by earth movements.

 When sedimentary rocks containing fossils are changed into metamorphic rocks, the fossils may change shape and become distorted.

 2 What makes sedimentary rocks start to change into metamorphic rocks?

The earth movements may force the rocks further down below the surface of the Earth. The inside of the Earth is very hot. The pressure from the earth movements and the higher temperature causes the rock to change. The sedimentary rock can be changed into metamorphic rock by the heat and pressure.

SEDIMENTARY ROCK

high temperature
high pressure

METAMORPHIC ROCK

Metamorphic rocks can also be formed around **magma** (molten rock) in the Earth's crust. The heat from the magma changes the rocks around it.

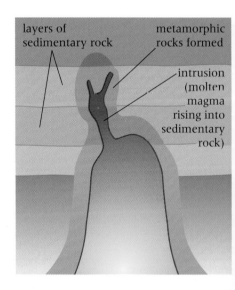

layers of sedimentary rock

metamorphic rocks formed

intrusion (molten magma rising into sedimentary rock)

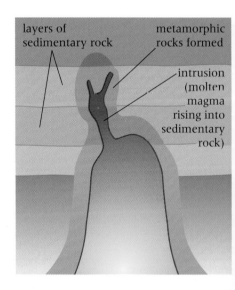 **3** Describe two ways in which metamorphic rocks can be formed.

When a rock changes, the properties of the rock change as well.

 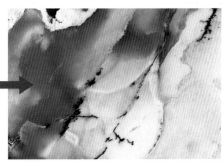 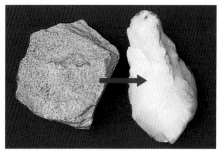

Limestone is a sedimentary rock. It feels rough and it can be porous. Porous rocks can soak up water because there are tiny gaps between the grains of rock.

Marble is a metamorphic rock formed when limestone is compressed and heated. It Is very different from limestone. Marble is hard and smooth, and it is not porous. The grains of rock in the limestone have changed into crystals.

*Sandstone turns into **quartzite** when it is heated and squashed. Quartzite is much harder than sandstone.*

Slate can be split into thin sheets because the cystals are lined up in the same direction. This does not happen when marble and quartzite are formed, so these rocks have a different texture.

4 Name two sedimentary rocks and the metamorphic rocks they change into.

5 Describe how you can tell a metamorphic rock from a sedimentary rock.

*The sedimentary rock, **shale**, turns into the metamorphic rock, slate.*

P How would you examine the differences between a metamorphic rock and the sedimentary rock from which it was made? Investigate several pairs of rocks.
● Do you find the same differences for all your pairs of rocks?

6 Which would be easier to carve into a statue – a sedimentary or a metamorphic rock? Explain your answer.

You should know...
● Metamorphic rocks are made from other types of rocks.
● These changes happen because of the high pressure caused by earth movements and high temperature inside the Earth.

How are igneous rocks formed?

The solid rocks we live on are called the **crust**. Underneath the crust is a layer called the **mantle**. The Earth is very hot inside. Sometimes the mantle and crust become so hot that they melt. The molten rock is called magma.

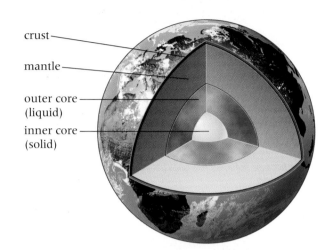

crust
mantle
outer core (liquid)
inner core (solid)

 1 What is magma?

When magma cools down it forms **igneous rocks**. Igneous rocks can look very different from each other. If magma cools down fast, it forms rocks containing small **crystals**. This can happen when magma flows out of the Earth's crust in a **volcano**. Magma that reaches the Earth's surface is called **lava**. Lava cools quickly in the air. If magma gets trapped underground it cools much more slowly. This forms rocks containing large crystals.

Basalt *has very small crystals.*

Granite *has large crystals.*

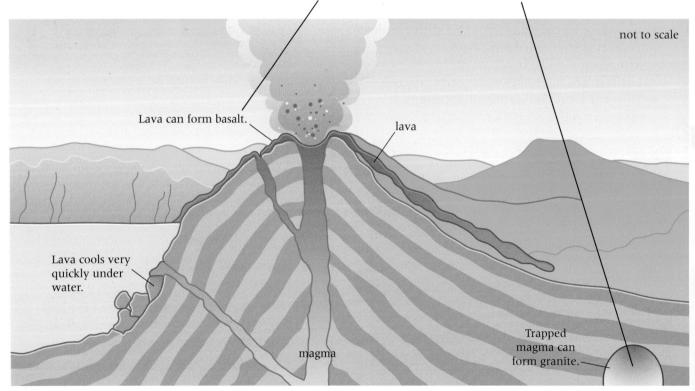

not to scale

Lava can form basalt.

lava

Lava cools very quickly under water.

magma

Trapped magma can form granite.

2 What is the difference between lava and magma?

2 What is the difference between lava and magma?

3 a) How is granite formed?
   b) How could you tell this by looking at a lump of granite?

4 Describe one way in which igneous rocks are different from sedimentary rocks.

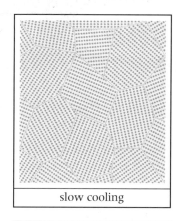

slow cooling

We can explain the difference in the crystal sizes by thinking about what happens to the **particles** in melted rock. When the rock is a liquid, the particles are free to move about. As the liquid cools down, **bonds** form between the particles. The bonds stick the particles together. As more bonds form, the particles become fixed in their positions. The particles are completely fixed in place when the crystals are solid.

If the rock cools down slowly, there will be time for lots of particles to move and stick together (bond) in an ordered arrangement, making large crystals. If the rock cools down quickly there will only be time for a few particles to bond in an ordered arrangement, so smaller crystals will be made.

fast cooling

A TV company wants to make a programme to show how the sizes of granite crystals are different depending on how fast they have cooled. They can't use granite because it is too difficult to melt. How could you investigate this using another chemical?
• Should the chemical that you use have a higher or lower melting point than granite?

5 a) Why can particles move in melted rock?
   b) What happens to the particles as the liquid rock starts to cool down?
   c) Why do some rocks have bigger crystals than others?

6 Why does magma cool more slowly than lava?

Fred argues that some igneous rocks are more dense than others because they contain different minerals. He says that gabbro-type rocks are more dense than granite-type rocks.
• How would you check whether he is correct?
• What about basalt and obsidian?

You should know...

● Magma cools to form igneous rocks.

● The faster the magma cools, the smaller the rock crystals are.

● The size of the crystals can be explained using ideas about particles.

What is the rock cycle?

The outer part of the Earth is continually changing, with rocks being weathered away and new rocks being formed. These processes have been going on since the Earth was formed.

The processes which make sedimentary, metamorphic and igneous rocks are linked together, forming a cycle which is never ending. Some processes in the **rock cycle** are quick, but most are so slow that we do not notice that they are happening.

The rock cycle.

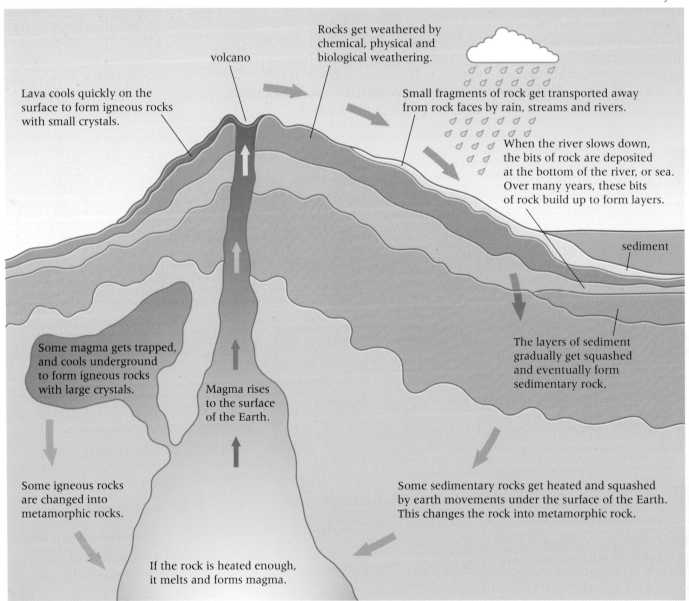

volcano

Rocks get weathered by chemical, physical and biological weathering.

Lava cools quickly on the surface to form igneous rocks with small crystals.

Small fragments of rock get transported away from rock faces by rain, streams and rivers.

When the river slows down, the bits of rock are deposited at the bottom of the river, or sea. Over many years, these bits of rock build up to form layers.

sediment

Some magma gets trapped, and cools underground to form igneous rocks with large crystals.

Magma rises to the surface of the Earth.

The layers of sediment gradually get squashed and eventually form sedimentary rock.

Some igneous rocks are changed into metamorphic rocks.

Some sedimentary rocks get heated and squashed by earth movements under the surface of the Earth. This changes the rock into metamorphic rock.

If the rock is heated enough, it melts and forms magma.

1 How are sedimentary rocks formed?

2 How are igneous rocks formed?

3 How are metamorphic rocks formed?

The rock cycle has been making and changing rocks since the Earth was formed. Humans have made more changes to the Earth. Many of the rocks and minerals formed by the rock cycle can be useful. Useful rocks such as limestone (a sedimentary rock) and slate (a metamorphic rock) are found near to the Earth's surface and can be removed by quarrying.

Some useful rocks and minerals are found deeper underground and may need to be extracted by mining. Other products of the rock cycle are found on the surface of the Earth. Sediments such as sand and gravel are found at the bottom of existing and dried up river beds. These can be removed very easily.

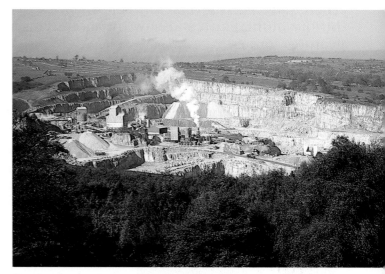

Quarries often leave permanent scars on the landscape.

4 How have humans changed the Earth?

5 Why are some products of the rock cycle quarried whereas others are mined?

6 Explain how sand and gravel deposits are formed.

While rocks are being formed, other rocks near to the surface of the Earth are being weathered by chemical, physical and biological processes. These processes include:
- the action of chemicals such as water and acidic rain
- the action of physical processes such as freeze-thaw and the contraction and expansion of rocks
- the biological action of plant roots growing into cracks in the rock.

The fragments of rocks produced are transported away and deposited as layers of sediment. In time these form new sedimentary rocks through compaction and cementation. All of these processes mean that the rock cycle never ends.

Extracting gravel from a gravel pit.

You should know...
- The Earth is continually changing.
- The rock cycle provides a continuous supply of new rock.
- The rock cycle links together all the processes involved in rock formation.

How is the history of the Earth explained by different theories?

There have been several different theories to explain the history of the Earth and how the mountains and other features formed.

Creationism

The formation of the Earth is described in the Book of Genesis in the Old Testament of the Bible. According to the Bible, the process of creation took six days. Many Christians recognise that the length of a day may not have been 24 hours and that it is the order of events which is more important. Calculations by James Ussher in 1640, using the Biblical account, gave the Earth an age of about 6000 years.

James Hutton (1726–1797).

Catastrophism

The catastrophe theory suggested that the shape of the surface of the Earth was formed by a series of sudden catastrophes. According to the supporters of this theory, such as Peter Pallas (1741–1811) and Jean Baptiste de Beaumont (1798–1874), these catastrophes were violent events, like huge earthquakes, which changed the landscape of the Earth.

Uniformitarianism

This theory about the Earth was developed by James Hutton in the late eighteenth century. Hutton suggested that we might be able to find out about the origin of ancient rocks by studying 'present-day' events such as weathering, transportation and sedimentation. He thought that the same processes had been occurring since the Earth was formed. Hutton was the first person to consider that changes in our landscape take many thousands or millions of years to happen – 'geological time' is very long.

Charles Lyell (1797–1875) developed Hutton's ideas and presented the idea of Uniformitarianism in his book, *Principles of Geology*.

1 Write down the names of the three theories that try to explain how mountains and other features were formed. Write one or two sentences to describe each theory.

2 What do you think is meant by 'geological time'?

3 Why do you think people no longer think that catastrophism can explain all Earth processes?

Plate tectonics

What happens on the Earth's surface?

The theory of **plate tectonics** suggests that the outer part of the Earth is made up of pieces, called **plates**, which are moved about very slowly by currents in the magma beneath.

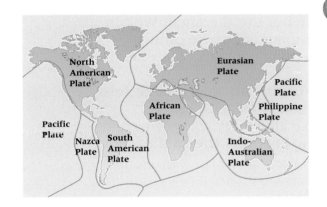

> ! The Himalaya mountains are still growing! They were formed when the Indo-Australian Plate hit the Eurasian Plate. The Indo-Australian Plate is still moving north at a speed of about 2 cm every year, making the Himalayas about 5 mm taller each year.

The moving plates can cause earthquakes.

Magma rising to the surface forms volcanoes.

Some of the crust melts and the magma rises.

When two continents get pushed together, mountains are formed.

One plate is pushed under another. This is called a **destructive plate margin**.

Magma forms new crust where the plates are moving apart. This is a **constructive plate margin**.

One piece of evidence to support the theory of plate tectonics are the shapes of Africa and South America. The shapes of the modern continents fit together nicely, and rocks on either side of the Atlantic Ocean match up. The same fossils have even been found in Africa and South America, suggesting that they were once joined together.

1 What is a plate?

2 What is a constructive plate margin?

3 What is a destructive plate margin?

4 How would you know if you were living near a destructive plate margin?

5 Research and write a report on the theory of plate tectonics, giving an account of the evidence that supports the theory.

then...

now...

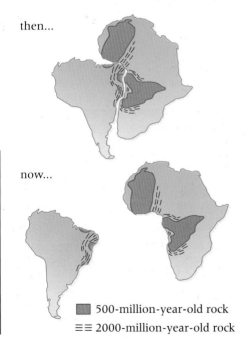

▨ 500-million-year-old rock
≡≡ 2000-million-year-old rock

103

What is the difference between heat and temperature?

Heat and **temperature** are related but not the same. We can measure temperature with a thermometer but we cannot measure the amount of heat something contains with one. This may sound strange but:

- Temperature describes how hot or cold an object is and it is usually measured in **degrees Celsius (°C)**.
- Heat is a form of energy and, like all energy, is measured in **joules (J)**. Another name for heat energy is **thermal** energy.

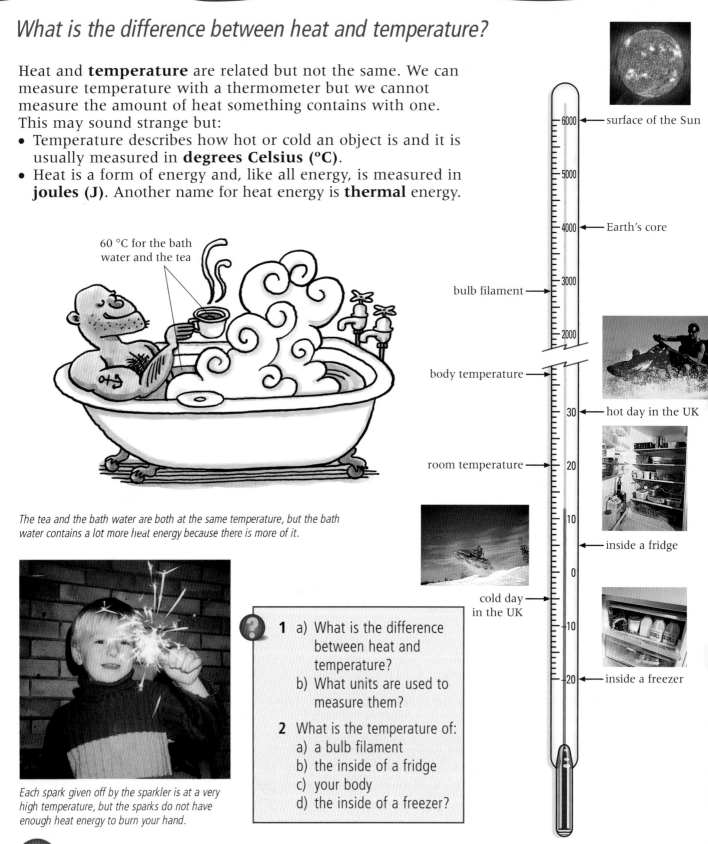

60 °C for the bath water and the tea

The tea and the bath water are both at the same temperature, but the bath water contains a lot more heat energy because there is more of it.

surface of the Sun — 6000

5000

Earth's core — 4000

3000

bulb filament → 2000

body temperature →

hot day in the UK — 30

room temperature → 20

10

inside a fridge

0

cold day in the UK — 10

inside a freezer — 20

Each spark given off by the sparkler is at a very high temperature, but the sparks do not have enough heat energy to burn your hand.

1 a) What is the difference between heat and temperature?
   b) What units are used to measure them?

2 What is the temperature of:
   a) a bulb filament
   b) the inside of a fridge
   c) your body
   d) the inside of a freezer?

The highest ever temperature recorded in the shade was on 13th September 1922 at Al'Aziziyah, Libya, in the Sahara Desert. It was 58°C. The lowest temperature recorded was −89.2°C in Antarctica during July 1983.

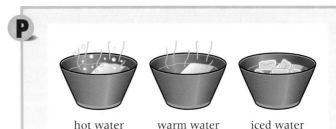

hot water   warm water   iced water

Is our skin a reliable way to tell how hot something is?
- Work in pairs to compare how hot you think the different bowls of water are.

It takes two minutes to heat the water in the kettle to 60°C. It takes over an hour to heat the hot water tank to 60°C. The hot water in the tank contains more heat energy than the water in the kettle because there is a lot more water.

3 a) Where is the hottest place on Earth?
   b) Where is the coldest place on Earth?

The amount of heat energy in something depends on three things:

- its temperature
- the material it is made from
- its mass.

Heat energy always flows from a hot object to a cool one. The cool object becomes hotter and the hot object becomes cooler until they are both at the same temperature.

4 Why does a bath full of hot water contain a lot more heat energy than a cup of tea at the same temperature?

5 Why don't you get burned by the sparks from a sparkler?

6 a) What happens to the temperature of a drink when you put an ice cube into it?
   b) What happens to the temperature of the ice cube?
   c) What will happen to the temperature of the drink if you leave it standing for a whole day?

You should know...

- The difference between temperature and heat.
- Thermal energy is another name for heat energy.
- Some examples of common temperatures.
- Heat energy flows from a hot object to a cooler one.

How is heat energy transferred through solids?

A **conductor** is something that lets energy flow through it. When heat energy travels through solids, this is called **conduction**. Some materials are better heat conductors than others. A poor heat conductor is called a heat **insulator**.

1 Copy these sentences and fill in the gaps.
Heat travels through _____
by _____. Materials that do not let heat travel through them easily are called _____.

You can tell whether something is a conductor or an insulator by touching it. If you walk around in your bare feet, tiles feel colder than carpets. This is because tiles are better heat conductors than carpets. The heat is conducted away from you quickly by the tiles, so your feet feel cold.

Carpets are good heat insulators because they contain trapped air. Air is a good heat insulator if it cannot move. The feathers on birds trap air and help to keep the birds warm. We can use feathers in duvets to keep us warm in bed.

P How could you decide which materials are good conductors and which are good insulators?
- Which materials would you test?
- How would you make your investigation fair?
- How could you use a temperature probe and computer to take measurements?

! Animals' fur keeps them warm because it traps air between the hairs and acts as an insulator. Polar bears' fur is an even better insulator, because it is made of hollow tubes so that even more air is trapped.

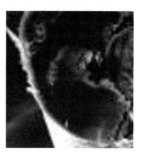

2 Why does a plastic fizzy drink bottle usually *feel* warmer than a metal can of drink even if they are at the same temperature?

3 Why is carpet a good insulator?

Wood and plastic are also good heat insulators so they are used for saucepan handles. The saucepan is made of metal because metals are good heat conductors and allow the heat to pass easily from the cooker into the food.

4 a) Why does a saucepan need to be made from a material that is a good conductor?
   b) Why are saucepan handles made from insulating materials?

5 Draw a table to show which of these materials are heat conductors, and which are heat insulators.
   wool   plastic   aluminium foil   wood   paper
   copper   air

The material on the outside of the Space Shuttle is a good heat insulator. When the shuttle is flying back to Earth the temperature can get as high as 1600 °C.

The particle model of matter can help to explain why some substances let heat flow through them easily and some do not.

When a solid is heated the particles in it gain energy and vibrate more. The particles bump into each other and pass the energy on. Conduction happens best in solids because the particles are very close together. Conduction does not take place very well in liquids, and hardly at all in gases.

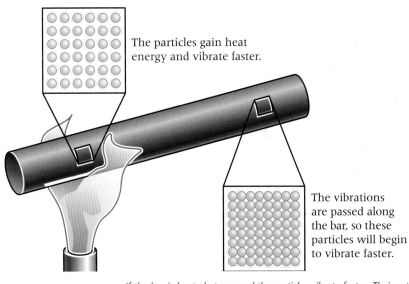

The particles gain heat energy and vibrate faster.

The vibrations are passed along the bar, so these particles will begin to vibrate faster.

If the bar is heated at one end the particles vibrate faster. Their extra movements are passed along the bar and **conduction** takes place.

6 Explain how heat is conducted through a solid object. Use ideas about particles in your answer.

7 Why are solids better heat conductors than liquids?

8 Why are gases heat insulators?

9 Find out what other forms of insulation animals have.

You should know...
- Heat energy passes through solids by conduction.
- Metals are good heat conductors.
- Insulators often contain pockets of trapped air.
- How conduction can be explained using the particle model.

What is the Kelvin temperature scale?

The hotter something gets, the faster its particles move. The temperature of a substance depends on the mean speed of its particles.

Temperature is measured with a thermometer. The scale on the thermometer is called a **temperature scale**. The **Celsius** and **Fahrenheit** scales are commonly used in the UK. Both scales are named after the scientists who first suggested them.

Celsius is the main scale used internationally, but scientists and engineers often use the **Kelvin** or **absolute scale** instead.

A weather map with temperatures in degrees Celsius and Fahrenheit.

In the nineteenth century an Englishman named Lord Kelvin (1824–1907) decided that it was inconvenient to use negative values when measuring very cold temperatures. In 1848 he proposed the Kelvin temperature scale. Like the Celsius scale, the Kelvin scale was based upon two fixed points: the freezing point of water, and the boiling point of water. However, Lord Kelvin set the zero for his scale on a different starting point. If a substance could be cooled down until all the particles stopped moving, it would be as cold as possible. The temperature would be **absolute zero**. Kelvin calculated that temperature to be –273 °C.

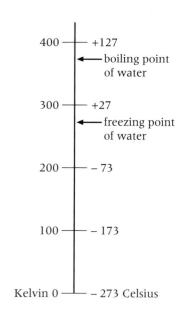

1 What does the 'temperature' of an object tell you about the movement of the particles in it?

2 What are the two fixed points on a Celsius or Kelvin thermometer scale?

3 Why did Lord Kelvin design a new scale?

4 What is absolute zero?

5 What is the freezing point of water on the Kelvin scale?

When writing a temperature in the Kelvin scale it is usual to leave out the ° symbol and just use the letter K. The boiling point of water is 100 °C or 373 K.

Changing size

Why do materials expand when they are heated?

When a solid is heated, the particles in it gain energy and vibrate more. The moving particles need more space to move around in and so the solid **expands** (gets bigger). When the solid cools down again the particles move more slowly and the solid **contracts** (gets smaller).

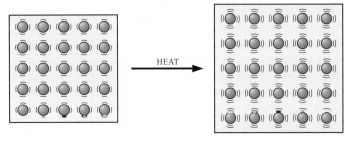

HEAT

When a solid expands it has the same mass, but takes up more space. Its density decreases.

1 Why do solids expand when they are heated?

A similar thing happens when liquids or gases are heated. The particles move around faster and so take up more room. The liquid or gas expands and its density decreases.

2 Why are bubbles of air coming out of the flask in the diagram on the right?

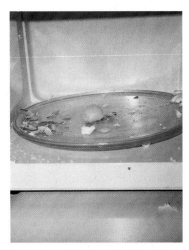

Eggs can explode if you heat them in their shells in a microwave oven.

Gases and some liquids are kept in sealed containers. The force of the particles hitting the walls of the container causes **pressure**. If the container is heated, the substance inside it gets hotter and the particles move faster. The substance cannot expand because it is in a sealed container. The moving particles hit the walls of the container harder, and the pressure increases. If the pressure gets high enough, the container may burst.

P

How can you use ideas about expanding liquids to make a thermometer?
- How will you know which temperatures it is showing?
- Explain how it works.

3 Explain how a thermometer works.

4 Explain why an egg will explode if you heat it too much.

You should know...
- **When particles are heated they move faster and take up more room.**
- **Substances expand when they are heated and contract when they are cooled.**

How does heat travel through liquids and gases?

Heat does not travel through liquids and gases very well by conduction, but it can travel by **convection**. The particles in liquids and gases can move around. Liquids and gases are all **fluids**.

When a fluid is heated, the particles move around faster. The fluid expands and it becomes less dense because the same amount of mass is taking up more space. If only part of the fluid is being heated, that part becomes less dense than the cooler fluid around it, and it starts to rise. Cooler fluid moves in to take its place, and a **convection current** forms.

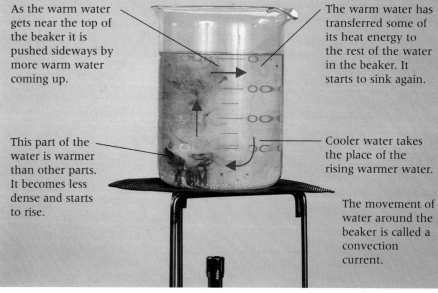

As the warm water gets near the top of the beaker it is pushed sideways by more warm water coming up.

The warm water has transferred some of its heat energy to the rest of the water in the beaker. It starts to sink again.

This part of the water is warmer than other parts. It becomes less dense and starts to rise.

Cooler water takes the place of the rising warmer water.

The movement of water around the beaker is called a convection current.

A purple dye can be used to show a convection current.

Convection currents can also form when part of a fluid is colder than its surroundings. An ice lolly will absorb energy from the air around it, and the air will cool down and sink.

1 a) What is a fluid?
   b) Write down three examples of fluids.

2 What happens to the density of a fluid when it is heated?

 Some birds use rising columns of warm air to keep them in the air. The highest altitude recorded for a bird was when a Ruppell's vulture hit an airliner at 11 300 m (11.3 km)!

3 Why will air sink if it is colder than the air around it?

4 Copy this diagram, and add arrows to show the direction of the convection current caused by the ice cube.

5 Use ideas about particles and convection to explain how a hot air balloon flies.

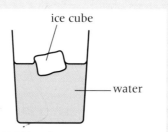

ice cube

water

You should know...

- Liquids and gases are called fluids.

- Heat is mainly transferred through fluids by convection.

- Convection currents can be formed by hot or cold objects.

How does heat travel from the Sun to the Earth?

There is nothing but empty space between the Sun and the Earth, so heat cannot travel from the Sun to the Earth by conduction or convection. All the heat we get from the Sun travels as **radiation** (sometimes called **infrared radiation**).

Infrared radiation travels as waves, like light waves. It does not need anything (a **medium**) to travel through, and it can also go through transparent substances like air or glass. Light and infrared radiation are similar in other ways as well.

1 Why can't heat energy travel through space by conduction or convection?

Heat and light from the flame radiate in all directions.

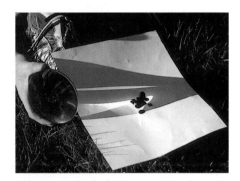
Infrared radiation and light can both be focused using a magnifying glass.

The shiny surface at the back of the heater reflects infrared radiation and light into the room.

All hot things give out or **emit** infrared radiation. When radiation hits something, it is taken into the object, or **absorbed**.

Thermal imagers are instruments that create pictures of heat rather than light. They measure infrared energy and convert the data into maps of temperatures. Thermal imaging can be used for filming things at night, and for finding the temperature of remote parts of the Earth by taking photographs from space.

The police use thermal imagers to help catch criminals.

2 Describe three ways in which infrared radiation and light are similar.

3 a) What is a thermal image?
b) Give one example of a thermal imager being used.

4 Design a table to show how heat can travel through transparent and opaque solids, liquids and gases. Use the words convection, conduction and radiation at the top of three columns of the table.

You should know...

● Heat can travel as infrared radiation.

● Infrared radiation does not need a medium to travel through.

How can we use less of our non-renewable fuels?

Fossil fuels (oil, coal, and natural gas) are used to generate electricity, for heating and for cooking. Fossil fuels are running out. If we use less of them then they will last longer.

If we stop some of the heat escaping from our homes we will use less fuel. We can do this by using materials that do not allow heat to go through them – **heat insulators**. Trapped air is a good heat insulator. Jumpers work because air is trapped and keeps you warm. Trapped air is also used in double glazing and loft insulation for houses.

 1 Write down the names of fossil fuels that are used for:
a) generating electricity
b) heating our homes
c) cooking.

 2 Look at the photograph. How can we tell which homes have loft insulation?

 How would you find out which insulating material is the best?
- How could you set up your equipment?
- How could you find out how much energy is lost?
- How would you make your experiment a fair test?
- How could you use a computer and temperature probes to record temperature measurements?

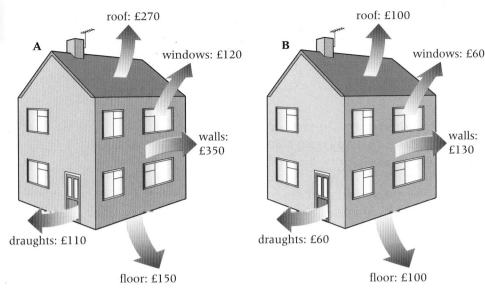

A

roof: £270
windows: £120
walls: £350
draughts: £110
floor: £150

B

roof: £100
windows: £60
walls: £130
draughts: £60
floor: £100

Houses lose different amounts of heat depending on how well insulated they are. This costs money in extra fuel bills.

Loft insulation comes in rolls of a material that has many pockets of trapped air.

Heat loss through windows can be reduced by using double glazing. This also cuts down on noise from roads.

Draught excluders are put around doors to stop draughts.

The space in between the walls of a house can be filled with a blown mineral wool.

You should know...

● **How heat loss can be reduced by using insulating materials containing trapped air.**

Look at the diagram of the two houses at the top of the page.

3 Which house has not been insulated?

4 a) For the uninsulated house, which part would you insulate first? Why?
b) Which method of insulation would you choose?

5 Explain how double glazing works.

6 Look at the photograph showing the INTEGER house.
a) How does the house absorb 'free' energy from the Sun?
b) How does the house keep in the heat it has absorbed?

This house, built by INTEGER at Garston in Hertfordshire, has many features to save energy.

How can we explain changes of state?

The three states of matter are **solids**, **liquids** and **gases**. We can change a solid into a liquid by heating it until it **melts**. The temperature when a solid becomes a liquid is called the **melting point** of the solid. The temperature when a liquid turns back into a solid is called the **freezing point**. The freezing point and melting point of a substance are always *the same* temperature.

1 a) What is the melting point of ice?
b) What is the freezing point of water?

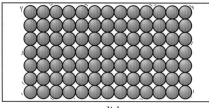
solid

Solids have particles that are close together. The particles are fixed in place and cannot swap places with each other. That is why solids have fixed shapes.

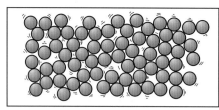
liquid

The particles in a liquid are still attached to one another but so weakly that they can move past each other. Liquids can change shape.

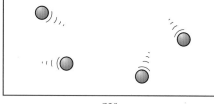
gas

In gases, the particles are not attached to each other and can move anywhere, by themselves. Gases can also change shape.

We can change a liquid into a gas by heating it. The liquid **evaporates** into a gas. The **boiling point** of a liquid is the temperature when it is evaporating as fast as it can.

We can change a gas into a liquid by cooling it down until the gas **condenses** into a liquid.

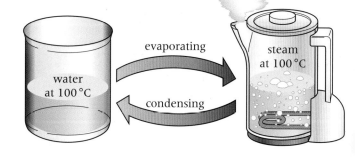
water at 100 °C
evaporating
condensing
steam at 100 °C

2 Iron and steel are solid materials. How could they be changed into liquids?

3 Oxygen is a gas. How could it be changed into a liquid?

How would you find out how the temperature changes when you heat or cool a substance?
- What will happen to the temperature when a solid is heated to its melting point?
- What will happen when the temperature reaches boiling point?
- Make a prediction by sketching a graph of temperature against time.
- What apparatus would you need?

If you plot a graph of temperature against time when you heat a pure substance, you get a graph like this.

> **4** a) What is the melting point of the substance shown in the graph?
> b) What is its freezing point?
> c) What is its boiling point?

Ice cubes can be used to make a drink cooler. For ice to melt it needs heat. The heat comes from the rest of the drink. The drink gives some of its heat energy to the ice cubes, so the drink gets colder. The ice cubes gain energy and turn from a solid into a liquid.

> **5** Where does the heat come from to melt an ice cube in a glass of water?

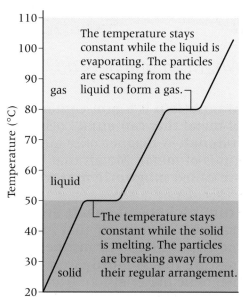

The temperature stays constant while the liquid is evaporating. The particles are escaping from the liquid to form a gas.

gas

liquid

solid

The temperature stays constant while the solid is melting. The particles are breaking away from their regular arrangement.

Temperature (°C)

Time (minutes)

Changing from a solid to a liquid needs **heat energy**. When a liquid turns back into a solid you get the heat energy back again. Dropping molten wax on your hand can be very painful. This is because the heat from the wax goes into your hand as it changes back into a solid.

> **6** Why is it painful if you drop molten wax on your hand? Explain as fully as you can.

Elephants live in hot countries. They often throw water over themselves.
- What will happen to the water?
- What experiment could you do to find out if they do this to help them cool down?
- What could you use to represent the elephant?
- What will you measure?
- How will you present your results?

> **7** Sketch a graph similar to the one above to show what happens when a substance cools down. Explain the shape of your graph.

You should know...
- The meanings of the words evaporating, condensing, freezing and melting.
- For any substance, the freezing point and melting point are the same.
- What happens to the particles when substances change state.

What can magnets do?

Magnetism is a non-contact force. A piece of metal that can attract other metals is a **magnet**. A magnet only attracts certain kinds of metal. Metals that can be attracted are called **magnetic materials**.

Iron, **nickel** and **cobalt** are all magnetic materials. A mixture that includes a magnetic material will also be magnetic. **Steel** is a mixture that is mostly iron, so it is a magnetic material too. Iron oxide is a compound that can be made into a magnet.

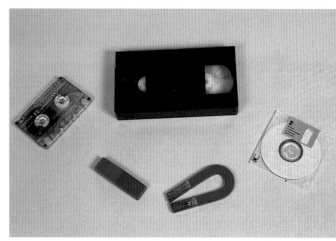

Bar magnets are made from metal. Computer discs and the tapes in video and music cassettes are coated with iron oxide.

 1 Which metals are magnetic materials?

2 Aluminium and steel can be recycled, but they must be separated first. Explain how you could use a magnet to separate aluminium cans from steel cans.

The two ends of a magnet are called the **north pole** and the **south pole**.

Magnets **attract** magnetic materials. Magnets can attract or **repel** (push away) other magnets.

You can only tell if something is a magnet by seeing if it will *repel* another magnet.

 3 What are the two ends of a magnet called?

4 Why can't you prove that something is a magnet by showing that it is attracted to another magnet?

 How could you find out when a magnet attracts and when it repels other magnets?

- The north pole of a magnet will attract the south pole of another magnet.
- A north pole will repel another north pole.
- A south pole will repel another south pole.

Fridge magnets will hold pieces of paper to a fridge door because the magnetism will act through the paper.

If a piece of magnetic material is put near to a magnet, the magnetism will not act through it.

You can make your own magnet, like this.

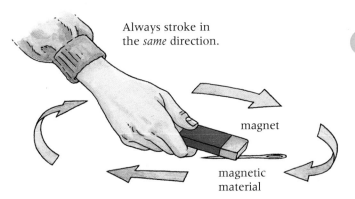

Always stroke in the *same* direction.

magnet

magnetic material

P How would you find out which materials magnetism can pass through?
- What equipment will you need?

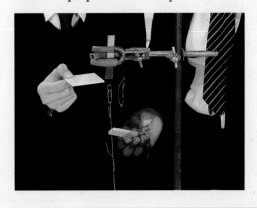

5 Write down the names of three materials that could stop magnetism.

6 Will these magnets attract or repel each other?

a)

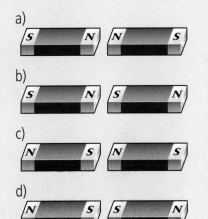

b)

c)

d)

You should know...
- Iron, nickel, cobalt, steel and iron oxide are all magnetic materials.
- When magnets attract and when they repel each other.

What are compasses?

If you go orienteering, or go walking in the countryside, you may need to use a **compass** to help you to find your way.

Magnetic materials were discovered hundreds of years ago. It was found that pieces of rock that contained a lot of iron would always point north if they were hung from a thread. A magnet that points north can be used as a compass.

When people made **bar magnets**, they named the end that pointed north the **north-seeking pole**. We call the other end of the magnet the **south-seeking pole**. These names are often shortened to **north pole** and **south pole**.

 Nobody knows when compasses were first used. Some people think that they were used in China over 2300 years ago, but compasses were certainly being used 800 years ago to help ships find their way.

French mariner's compass made in Marseille, France, in 1775.

P How can you make a compass using a magnet?
- How will you make sure your magnet can turn freely?

1 What is a compass?

2 Why is one end of a magnet called the north-seeking pole?

3 The Earth acts as if it has a bar magnet inside it. Copy this diagram and write N and S on the ends of the magnet inside the Earth. You may need to look back at page 117.

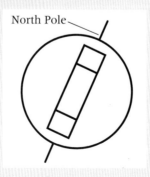
North Pole

You should know...
- A magnet that can move will always point north.
- The names for the two poles of a magnet.

William Gilbert

What did William Gilbert find out about magnetism?

William Gilbert (1544–1603) was a scientist and a physician (doctor). His father was wealthy enough to send him to the University of Cambridge to study, and Gilbert eventually became a lecturer there. In the 1570s he moved to London and became a physician. One of his patients was Queen Elizabeth I.

William Gilbert.

William Gilbert was interested in magnetism. Sailors had been using lodestones (pieces of magnetic rock) as compasses for hundreds of years to help them to find their route at sea, but no one knew why they worked.

A piece of lodestone.

Gilbert suggested that the Earth was itself a giant magnet, with its poles near the geographic poles of the Earth. This would explain why magnetic compass needles pointed north. He investigated ways of strengthening the magnetism of lodestones, and found out how to magnetise a piece of iron by stroking it. He also discovered that a magnet will lose its magnetism if it is heated.

Gilbert first published his findings in 1600. His book was called *De Magnete*, which means 'On magnets'. It was written in Latin, as that was the language used by educated people for writing books.

The title page of Gilbert's book.

1 Write down three things that Gilbert discovered about magnets.

2 What was Gilbert's theory to explain why compasses worked?

3 Why do you think there was a picture of a ship on the title page of Gilbert's book?

4 a) How would other scientists have found out about Gilbert's theories?

b) How can present-day scientists find out about new discoveries? Write down as many ways as you can.

What shape are magnetic fields?

A magnet can affect magnetic materials placed near it. The space around the magnet where it has an effect is called the **magnetic field**.

You can see the shape of the magnetic field of a bar magnet using **iron filings**.

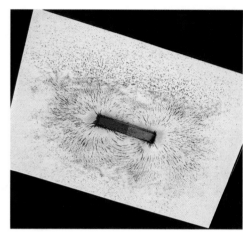

Iron filings being used to show the magnetic field

> **?** **1** What is a magnetic field?

You can also find the shape of a magnetic field using a small compass.

This compass is called a **plotting compass**. If there are no magnets near, it will point to the Earth's north.

If it is near a magnet, the compass will be affected by the magnetic field of the magnet.

Scientists draw the magnetic field of a bar magnet like this. If you look very carefully at the photograph of the iron filings, you can see that they are showing a similar shape.

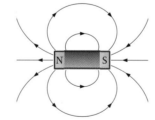

The field is all around the magnet. The magnetic field is strongest where the lines are close together.

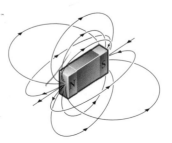

> **P** How could you plot the shape of the magnetic field of a bar magnet?
>
>

The magnetic field has a direction. This direction is the way the north pole of a compass moves near another magnet. North poles repel each other, so the direction of the magnetic field is *away* from the north pole of the bar magnet, and *towards* the south pole.

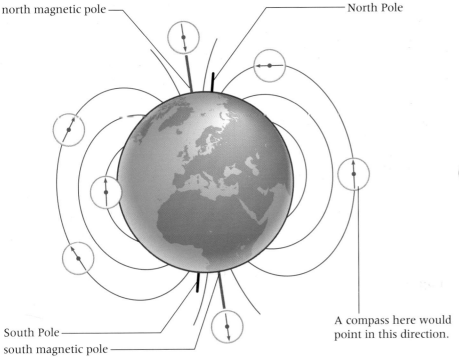

north magnetic pole

North Pole

South Pole

south magnetic pole

A compass here would point in this direction.

*Compasses point north because the Earth has a magnetic field. Compasses point towards the **north magnetic pole**, which is near the North Pole.*

2 Describe two ways of finding the shape of a magnetic field.

3 Draw the shape of the magnetic field around a bar magnet.

4 Which way will the north pole of a compass move if it is put near the north pole of a bar magnet?

You can make a magnet just by leaving a piece of iron or steel in a magnetic field. Steel things in your home like cans of food, or fridge doors, will eventually be magnetised by the Earth's magnetic field.

5 Sam has a compass. When he stands in the middle of the playing field it points north, but when he stands next to the school's metal gates it points in a different direction.
  a) Explain why Sam's compass points north when he stands in the middle of the field.
  b) Which metal do you think the school gates are made from?
  c) Why did Sam's compass point in a different direction near the gates?

P What shape is the magnetic field when two bar magnets are placed next to each other?
• How would you find out?
• How many different ways are there for you to arrange your two magnets?

You should know...

● **The space around a magnet where it has an effect is the magnetic field.**

● **The direction of a magnetic field is away from the north pole of a magnet and towards the south pole of a magnet.**

● **The Earth has a magnetic field.**

How can electromagnets be used to make sounds?

When electricity flows through a coil of wire, the coil acts like a magnet. A magnet made using electricity is called an **electromagnet**.

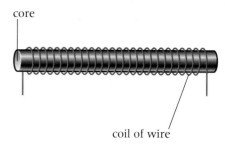
core

coil of wire

An electromagnet.

1 a) What happens to the magnetic field of an electromagnet if you switch the current off?
   b) How is this different to a bar magnet?
   c) Why do you think bar magnets are sometimes called **permanent magnets**?

You can change the strength of an electromagnet by:
- changing the number of coils of wire
- changing the current in the wire
- changing the material used for the core.

Electromagnets can be used to lift objects made of magnetic materials. They can also be used in bells and buzzers to make sounds.

P How could you make a very strong electromagnet?
- Which variables would you investigate?
- How would you make your investigation a fair test?
- How would you test the strength of your electromagnet?

2 Which materials could an electromagnet pick up?

3 How could you make a very strong electromagnet? There are three things you would have to do.

This photograph shows the inside of an electric bell. The armature is a piece of iron that is hinged at one end. It is attracted towards the electromagnets when they are switched on.

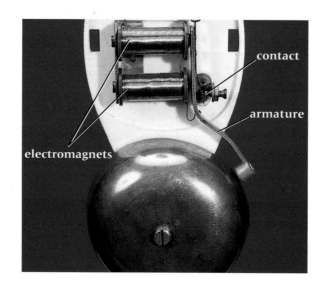
contact

armature

electromagnets

This is the circuit for an electric bell. The red line shows where the electric current flows when someone is pressing the button.

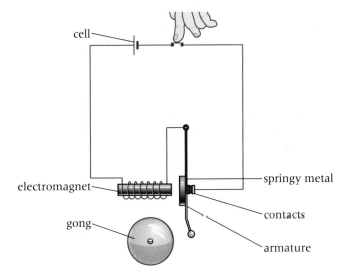

4 Describe the path of the current from the cell around the circuit.

5 a) What will happen when the current flows around the electromagnet?
   b) What will this do to the armature?

This diagram shows the circuit just after it has been switched on. The current flowing through the electromagnet has made a magnetic field. The armature is attracted to the electromagnet, and breaks the circuit at the contacts. The end of the armature hits the gong and makes a noise.

When the circuit is broken no current can flow, so the magnetic field disappears and the springy metal pulls the armature back to the contacts. When the contacts are closed the current can flow again, which magnetises the electromagnet, and attracts the armature. The armature keeps springing backwards and forwards as long as someone has a finger on the button.

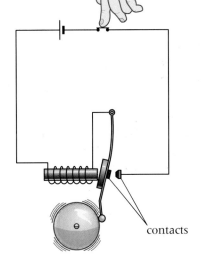

6 Look at the diagrams of the electric bell circuit. When the current stops:
   a) what happens to the magnetic field around the electromagnet
   b) what happens to the armature
   c) what happens to the contacts?

7 The kind of switch used in the bell is called a **make and break switch**. Why do you think it has this name?

You should know...

● **How to change the strength of an electromagnet.**

● **How an electric bell works.**

What are relays and why are they useful?

Electromagnets can be used to switch things on or off. A switch that is turned on or off by an electromagnet is called a **relay**.

You can make a relay using a **reed switch**. A reed switch has two thin pieces of magnetic material inside, called reeds. There is normally a gap between the two reeds. If a magnet, or an electromagnet, is put close to the reed switch, the reeds become magnetised. They attract each other. When they touch, the switch is closed and an electric current can flow through it.

 1 a) What are the reeds in a reed switch made from?
b) What happens to the switch when a magnet is near it?

Other kinds of relay switches use an electromagnet to attract a piece of iron. An electromagnet is usually called a **solenoid** when it is used in a relay. Relays can be used to make safe switches.

These diagrams show the starter motor circuits in a car. There are two circuits.

The starter motor uses a large current, so it is connected to the battery with thick wires.

The current to the starter motor is switched on and off using a relay. The relay is put close to the starter motor so that the thick wires do not need to be very long. This helps to save money when building the car.

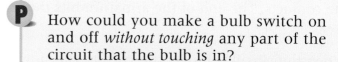 **P** How could you make a bulb switch on and off *without touching* any part of the circuit that the bulb is in?

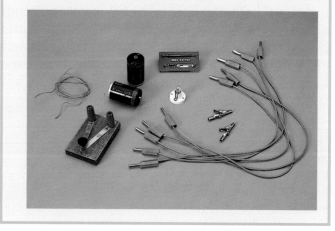

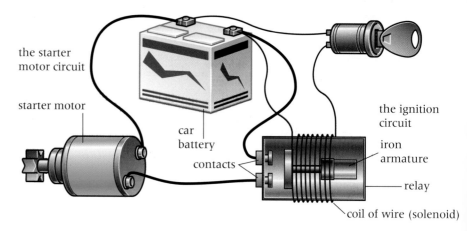

the starter motor circuit

starter motor

car battery

contacts

the ignition circuit

iron armature

relay

coil of wire (solenoid)

When the driver turns the key in the ignition circuit a current flows in the electromagnet. The iron **armature** is attracted by the solenoid, and closes the switch in the starter motor circuit. Only a small current flows in the ignition circuit, so the wires can be quite thin.

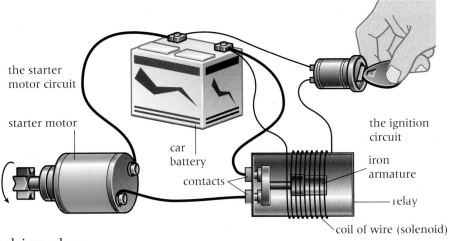

the starter motor circuit

starter motor

car battery

contacts

the ignition circuit

iron armature

relay

coil of wire (solenoid)

This arrangement means that the driver does not have to touch any part of the circuit that has a high current flowing through it. This makes it safer.

2 Copy these sentences and fill in the gaps using words from the box.

> armature   circuit   contacts
> solenoid   small

When the driver turns the ignition key a _____ current flows in the _____. This attracts the iron _____. The end of the armature joins the two _____, so that a current can flow in the starter motor _____.

3 How does using a relay in a car starter motor circuit make the car safer?

4 This diagram shows a relay used to switch on the floodlights at a football ground.

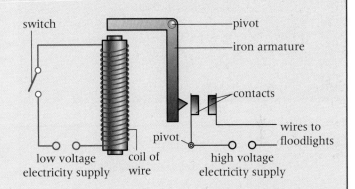

switch

pivot

iron armature

contacts

wires to floodlights

pivot

low voltage electricity supply

coil of wire

high voltage electricity supply

a) Why is it safer to use a relay to switch on the lights?
b) What happens to the coil of wire when someone presses the switch?
c) What happens to the iron armature?
d) How does this switch on the floodlights?
e) Why is iron used for the armature?

You should know...

● **How reed switches work.**

● **What a relay is and how it works.**

● **Why relays are useful.**

How do electromagnets work?

If you hold a compass close to a wire with an electric current flowing through it, the compass needle will move. The current produces a magnetic field around the wire.

An electromagnet has a magnetic field. The shape of the field is similar to the magnetic field of a bar magnet. You can show the shape of the field using iron filings or a plotting compass.

 Hans Christian Ørsted (1777–1851) discovered in 1820 that a compass needle can be affected by an electric current in a wire. He had discovered that electricity can cause magnetism.

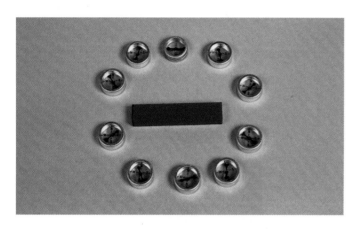

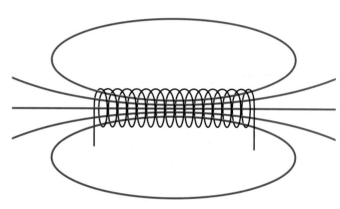

The shape of a magnetic field around an electromagnet.

 1 How could you change the direction in which a compass needle points using a cell and a piece of wire?

2 Describe two ways of finding the shape of the magnetic field of an electromagnet.

 Sound can be recorded using magnetism. A Danish engineer called Valdemar Poulsen (1869–1942) first recorded sound using a magnetised steel wire in 1898. Today electromagnets are used to record sound on plastic tapes coated with iron oxide.

Electromagnets often have a **core**. If the core is made of a magnetic material, it concentrates the magnetic field and makes the electromagnet stronger. Many electromagnets have cores made from iron.

You should know...

- An electric current produces a magnetic field.
- A coil of wire makes a magnetic field like the one around a bar magnet.
- How to change the strength of an electromagnet.

 3 a) Name two other metals that could be used for the core of an electromagnet.

b) Why is copper not a good material to use for the core of an electromagnet?

The field around a wire

What is the shape of the magnetic field around a wire?

This picture shows some plotting compasses around a wire. There is no electric current flowing in the wire, and the compasses are all pointing north.

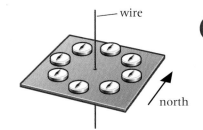
wire

north

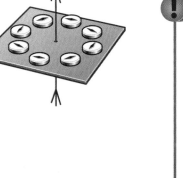

1 Why do the compasses point north before the current is switched on?

2 Describe the shape of the magnetic field around a wire with a current flowing through it.

When the current is switched on, the compasses change direction. The electric current has made a magnetic field. If you change the direction of the current, the direction of the magnetic field changes.

electric current

You can also see the shape of the magnetic field using iron filings.

You can change the shape of the magnetic field by changing the shape of the wire. If you make a loop in the wire, the magnetic field looks like this.

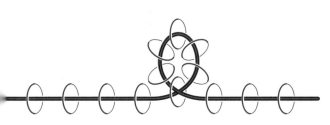

If you make a coil of wire with lots of loops, the magnetic field is concentrated inside the loops, and is much stronger. This is an **electromagnet**. Its magnetic field has a similar shape to the magnetic field of a bar magnet.

*This is a **maglev** train. When it is moving it does not touch the tracks. There are electromagnets in the train and the track which repel each other. The train floats (or levitates) on the magnetic fields.*

3 Why do you think an electromagnet is stronger if it has lots of coils?

4 A maglev train can be moved using electromagnets in the track.
a) Would the electromagnets in the track ahead of the train have to attract or repel the ones in the train?
b) What would have to happen to the electromagnets in the track as the train reached them? Explain your answer.
c) How could the direction of the magnetic fields of the electromagnets be changed?

What is light and how does it move?

There is light all around us and we cannot see anything without it. Objects that create light are **sources** of light or **luminous sources**. We can see non-luminous objects because light bounces off them and enters our eyes.

> **1** Look around the room you are in at the moment.
> a) Name two luminous sources.
> b) Name two non-luminous things that light is bouncing off.

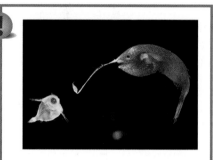

Angler fish live deep in the ocean where it is dark. They have luminous sources attached to them to attract other fish which they eat.

As soon as you switch on a lamp you can see the light. The light actually takes time to travel from the lamp to your eyes but it is too fast for you to notice.

Hundreds of years ago people thought that light did not travel. It was either on or off. They thought this because they could see the lightning in a thunderstorm straight away but the sound of the thunder took longer to reach them.

You see the lightning before you hear the sound of thunder. For every three seconds between the flash of lightning and the sound of thunder, the storm is about one kilometre away.

The Italian scientist Galileo (1564–1642) said that thunderstorms did not prove that light was only on or off, only that light travels faster than sound. He tried to measure the speed of light by shining lanterns a mile apart. However, light travels so fast he could not work out a speed. You need a much bigger distance to notice the delay between light leaving one point and reaching another.

> **2** a) Sound, like light, is another form of energy. Which travels faster, light or sound?
> b) How can you tell this?

Olaus Roemer (1644–1710), a Dutch scientist, was the first to measure the speed of light in 1675. He worked out the speed of light by observing the moons of Jupiter at different times in Jupiter's orbit.

Light travels at 300 000 km/s. It takes 8.5 minutes for light from the Sun to reach the Earth and 1.3 seconds for light bouncing off our Moon to reach the Earth. It takes four years for light to travel from the nearest star (apart from the Sun), a distance of 40 million million km.

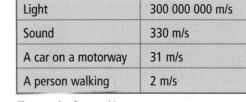

3 Which luminous source in the Solar System did the light bouncing off Jupiter's moons in Roemer's observations come from?

Light	300 000 000 m/s
Sound	330 m/s
A car on a motorway	31 m/s
A person walking	2 m/s

The speeds of some things.

4 How long does it take for light to travel from the Sun to the Moon and then to the Earth? Give your answer in seconds.

5 Why does light from the stars take longer to reach the Earth than light from the Sun?

Light travels in straight lines. **Shadows** are made because light cannot travel through some objects. The light cannot bend around them either.

A **laser** gives out a narrow beam of light. We can see the path of the light because the light bounces off the dust in the air. Lasers also show that light travels in straight lines. On diagrams, we show the straight lines that light takes by drawing **rays**.

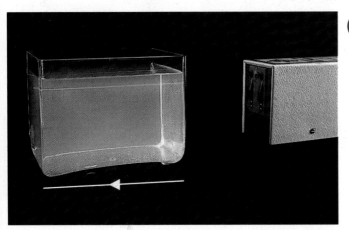

6 How do we know that light travels in straight lines?

7 Describe a laser beam.

8 Why can we see the light from a laser beam?

You should know...
- **Light travels in straight lines which can be shown by rays on a diagram.**
- **Light travels faster than sound.**

The liquid in this tank has a lot of particles in it. The laser light bounces off the particles so we can see it. A ray is drawn below the tank. It is a straight line and shows the direction the light travels in.

What happens when light hits something?

When light hits an object, different things can happen to it depending on what the object is made out of. Light travels through **transparent** materials like glass. Sometimes you can only see a glow of light through something. We say that materials like this are **translucent**. Paper is translucent. Things that light cannot travel through are called **opaque**. Opaque objects cause shadows.

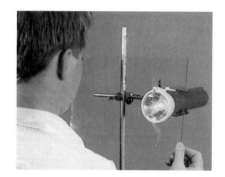
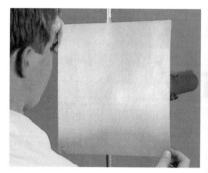

Light passing through an object is said to be **transmitted**. Transparent objects transmit more light than translucent objects. Light bounces off other objects. We say that the light is **reflected** and this is how we see non-luminous objects.

> **?** 1 Name two things which are:
> a) opaque   b) transparent   c) translucent.

> **?** 2 Look at the photograph on the right.
> a) Which luminous source is the man looking at?
> b) Which object is reflecting light into the dog's eyes?
> c) How can the man see the popcorn?

> **P** How would you use a ray box to classify materials as transparent, translucent or opaque?
> • Could you use a datalogger to compare the amount of light reflected or transmitted?

Light is also 'taken in' or **absorbed** by some objects. Darker objects absorb more light than paler ones. The white background of this page looks bright because it is reflecting light but the black letters look dark because they are absorbing it. Many objects both absorb and reflect light.

> **?** 3 Which will absorb more light: a dark brown coat or a pale blue coat?
>
> 4 Which will transmit more light: a piece of clear glass of a piece of paper?

> **You should know...**
> ● Materials can be transparent, translucent or opaque.
> ● Light can be transmitted through things, absorbed by them or reflected by them.

Eyes and cameras

How do eyes and cameras work?

You see things because light from them enters your eyes.

> **1** a) What energy change happens in your eyes?
> b) Where does this energy change happen?

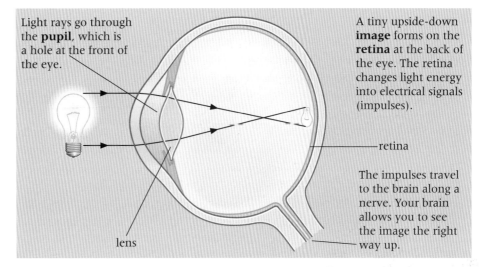

Light rays go through the **pupil**, which is a hole at the front of the eye.

A tiny upside-down **image** forms on the **retina** at the back of the eye. The retina changes light energy into electrical signals (impulses).

retina

The impulses travel to the brain along a nerve. Your brain allows you to see the image the right way up.

lens

Cameras work in a similar way to eyes. The simplest kind of camera is a **pinhole camera**. It does not have any lenses. It is called a pinhole camera because the hole can be made with a pin and is very small. The **image** forms on a screen at the back of the camera.

> **2** What is a pinhole camera?
> **3** What is the picture called which forms in the camera?
> **4** Name two ways in which the eye and a camera are similar.

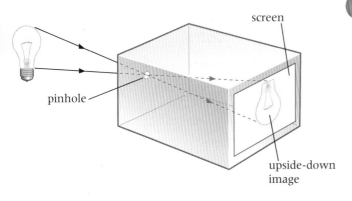

screen

pinhole

upside-down image

The hole in the front of a camera can be made bigger or smaller to control how much light gets in. Your eyes work in a similar way. Too much light can damage your eyes, so the pupil gets smaller when it is very bright. In dim light the pupil gets bigger to let in more light.

> **5** Why do the pupils in your eyes change size?

This view from a window was the world's first photograph, taken in 1826. It was recorded on a pewter plate and took several hours to take.

Even though photography improved, at the end of the 1800s it still took a long time to take photographs of people. They often had to stand in wire frames to keep them still.

What happens to the light when we look in the mirror?

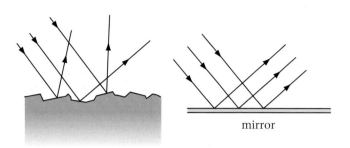

mirror

We see things when light bounces off them and enters our eyes. Most things **reflect** light in all directions. A mirror is very smooth, and reflects light evenly. We can see an **image** in a mirror.

A **plane mirror** is a flat shiny mirror. It is usually made of glass with a thin layer of silver or aluminium on the back.

Your teeth are not as smooth as the mirror. Teeth scatter light in all directions. A dentist cannot see his reflection in your teeth.

The mirror reflects the light evenly to produce an image. The dentist can see a reflection of your teeth in the mirror.

1 Why can't you see an image on a piece of paper?

2 a) What is a flat mirror called?
   b) What is it made from?

- The ray of light which goes to the mirror is the **incident ray**.

- The ray of light which comes from the mirror is the **reflected ray**.

- The **normal** is a line which is drawn as a dashed line at right angles to the mirror. It helps us to measure the angles.

- The **angle of incidence** is the angle between the **incident ray** and the **normal**.

- The **angle of reflection** is the angle between the **reflected ray** and the **normal**.

incident ray

angle of incidence

normal

plane (flat) mirror

reflected ray

angle of reflection

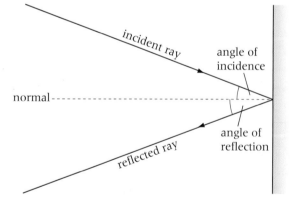

P How would you find out whether there is a relationship between the angle of incidence and the angle of reflection?

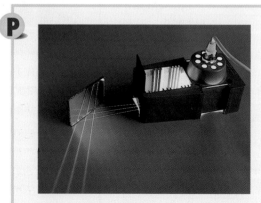

This **ray diagram** shows how we see an image in a mirror. Rays of light spread out in all directions from a luminous source. When we draw ray diagrams we only draw two rays, to keep the diagram simple.

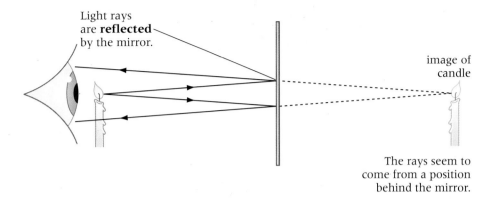

Light rays are **reflected** by the mirror.

image of candle

The rays seem to come from a position behind the mirror.

Some rules for reflections in a plane mirror

- The **angle of incidence** is equal to the **angle of reflection**. This means that the ray leaves the mirror at the same angle it arrived at the mirror.
- The image is the *same size* as the object.
- The image is the *same distance* from the mirror as the object.
- In the image, left is right and right becomes left.

3 If you raise your right hand and look in a mirror, which hand does your image raise?

4 If you stand 4 m from a mirror, how far are you from where the image appears to be?

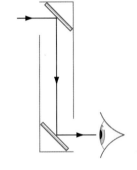

A periscope uses two mirrors. You can use a periscope to see over things.

5 Give four uses of plane mirrors.

A kaleidoscope is a toy that uses mirrors to make lots of reflections of something. This photograph shows a person inside a giant kaleidoscope.

Mirrors are used to see into places that can't be viewed directly.

You should know...

- Smooth surfaces reflect light evenly, and other surfaces reflect light in all directions.
- The angle of incidence is equal to the angle of reflection.

How do we bend light?

Light changes direction when it goes from one substance to another. This happens when light goes from air to water, or glass to air, or the other way round. This bending of light is called **refraction**. It only takes place at the boundary or **interface** between the substances.

1 What is refraction?

2 Explain why the pencil in the photograph appears to bend.

A **ray diagram** showing what happens when light bends is shown on the right. A dashed line called the normal is drawn at right angles to the surface where the ray enters. The angle between the light ray and the normal is called the **angle of incidence**. The angle between the ray and the normal as it passes through the surface is called the **angle of refraction**.

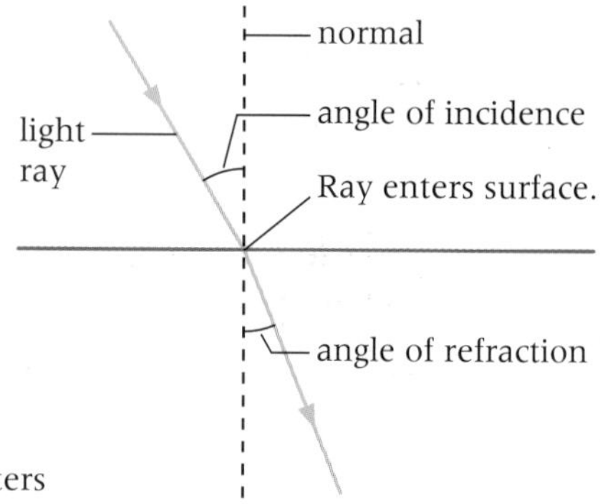

normal
angle of incidence
light ray
Ray enters surface.
angle of refraction

When light travels from air to a denser material such as glass or water it bends towards the normal. When it travels out into the air it bends away from the normal.

The reason that light changes direction when it passes from one medium to another is that it travels more slowly in denser substances.

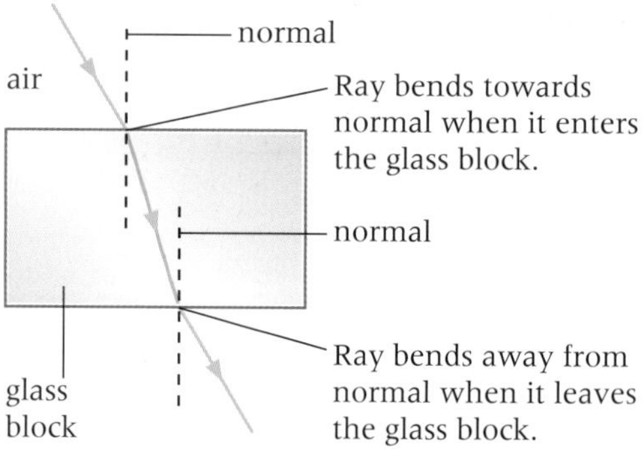

normal
air
Ray bends towards normal when it enters the glass block.
normal
Ray bends away from normal when it leaves the glass block.
glass block

When a car hits a deep patch of mud the wheel that hits the mud is slowed down but the other continues at the same speed and the car is swung round.

The bowl and the water are refracting light.

How would you investigate what happens when a ray of light goes into a glass block?
- What happens when it comes out again?

In 1621, a Dutch mathematician called Willebrod Snell (1580–1626) worked out a way of predicting how much a ray of light would be refracted. Unfortunately he did not tell anyone about his discovery at the time! A French mathematician called René Descartes (1596–1650) worked it out again in 1637.

3 Draw a ray diagram to explain what the following are:
a) the normal
b) the angle of incidence
c) the angle of refraction.

4 a) Which is denser, glass or air?
b) How does the density of a material affect the speed at which light travels through it?

5 Copy these sentences and fill in the gaps.
When light passes into or out of glass, the rays change _____. This change of direction is called _____.

6 The disappearing coin trick works by refraction.
a) Copy the two lower diagrams and complete the second one.
b) Explain how the trick works.

The coin trick.

The coin is invisible.

You can see the coin.

You cannot see the coin in this cup.

If you keep your head still and someone pours water into the cup, you can see the coin.

Mirages are caused by refraction. Sometimes on a sunny day it appears that there is water on the road as you are driving along. The driver appears to see blue ahead on the road. We are used to seeing the sky reflected in water so it looks like water to us.

You should know...
- That light changes direction at the interface of two different substances.
- Some effects of refraction.

How can you reflect light without a mirror?

When light rays go into a glass block they do not always pass right through the block. Sometimes some of the light is **reflected** and some of it is **refracted**.

If the ray enters at a particular angle the ray is completely **reflected**. This is called **total internal reflection** because the reflection happens *inside* the glass.

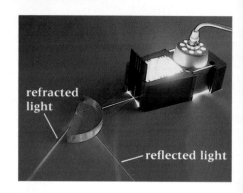
refracted light
reflected light

Uses of total internal reflection

The triangular piece of glass in a cat's eye is a **prism**. When light rays enter the prism at the correct angle, light is reflected back to the road user.

A cat's eye.

Doctors can use glass fibres to see into different parts of the body. Light is reflected from side to side along the glass fibre. When glass fibres are used like this they are called **optical fibres**.

A prism.

Prism or lens?

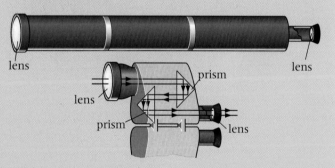
lens
lens
prism
prism
lens
lens

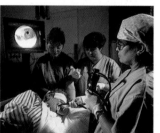
Doctors using optical fibres to see inside a patient's body.

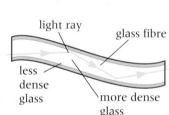
light ray
glass fibre
less dense glass
more dense glass
Light is reflected inside the optical fibre.

Most telescopes use two lenses to make a larger image, but the image is upside down.

Binoculars have two lenses and two prisms. The prisms send the light backwards and forwards three times so binoculars are shorter than a telescope of the same strength. The prisms also make the final image the right way up.

1 a) What does total internal reflection mean?
   b) Give two examples of total internal reflection.

2 What is the difference between refraction and reflection?

3 a) Give an example of helpful reflection to a driver.
   b) When could reflection be dangerous for a driver?

4 a) Why do bird watchers often use binoculars?
   b) Why do you think they do not use telescopes instead?

How do you split light?

We think of daylight as **white light**. But white light is made up of different colours. You can split up white light with a **prism**. This is usually a triangular block of glass or plastic.

When light passes through a prism it is split into colours. The different colours in white light are refracted (bent) by different amounts, so the colours spread out. The colours of the rainbow are called a **spectrum**. Red is refracted least and violet the most. This separating of the colours is called **dispersion**.

The colours in the spectrum are red, orange, yellow, green, blue, indigo, and violet. To help you remember the colours, the first letters of the spectrum colours spell out a name: ROY G BIV.

P

How would you make a spectrum using a prism?
● How could you get the different coloured rays to mix together again?

A rainbow is produced when water droplets in the air refract sunlight.

1 What is a prism?
2 List the colours in the spectrum.
3 How is a rainbow formed?

The rainbow was first explained by a German scientist, Theodoric (c.1250–c.1310), in the fourteenth century. He said that a rainbow was caused by the Sun's rays being refracted by rain or mist. Isaac Newton (1642–1727) carried out experiments with prisms at Cambridge University. He discovered how to split light in 1669. Most people can only see six colours in a spectrum, but Newton decided that there were seven colours because he thought that seven was a magic number!

You should know...

● **How white light is dispersed into a spectrum.**

How can you make white light?

When **red**, **green** and **blue** coloured lights are mixed, our eyes see them as white light. Red, green and blue are said to be the **primary colours** of light. All the other colours can be made from these three colours.

Where two colours overlap the **secondary colours** are made:

- Red and green make **yellow**.
- Red and blue make **magenta** (pronounced '*maj-**ent**-a*').
- Green and blue make **cyan** (pronounced '***sigh**-an*').

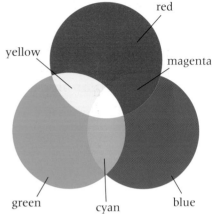

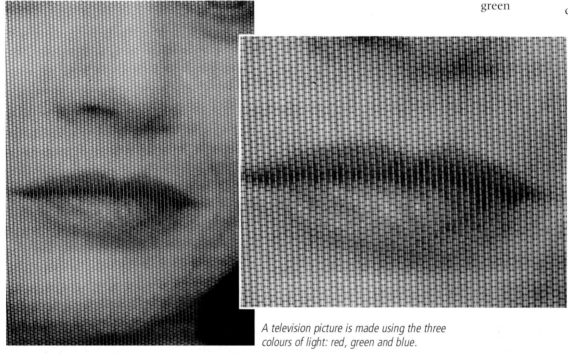

A television picture is made using the three colours of light: red, green and blue.

1 What are the three primary colours in light?

2 What are the secondary colours of light and how do you make them?

P How would you make white light by spinning a disc with different colours on it?

- What happens when you mix the secondary colours of light?
- What will happen when you combine other colours of light and patterns?

Making coloured light

Coloured light can be made using **filters**. As white light passes through a filter some of the colours are **absorbed**. A red filter only allows red light to be **transmitted** through the filter and all the other colours are absorbed.

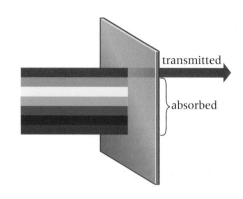

Many objects look coloured because they do not reflect all the colours in light. White objects reflect *all* the colours. A red object only reflects red light and all the other colours are absorbed. This idea applies to all colours except black. Black objects absorb *all* colours.

If a coloured light shines onto an object then the object's colour may appear to change. This is because there are fewer colours to be reflected.

3 Why do black objects appear black?

1 In white light player X's red top reflects only red light. Player Y's top reflects only blue. Player Y's shorts reflect all colours so they look white. Player X's shorts absorb all colours so they look black.

2 Only red light is hitting the white shorts so they can only reflect red. The blue top and black shorts absorb red so they look black.

3 Only blue light is hitting the white shorts so they can only reflect blue. The red top and black shorts absorb the blue light so they look black. The blue top still looks blue because it can reflect the blue light that is hitting it.

4 At an evening football match it was decided to use green lights to make it look more exciting. If one side wore green and the other red, what colour would they appear in the green lights?

5 Sam is wearing a white shirt, a red jacket and green trousers to a nightclub. What will his clothes look like:
a) in a red spotlight
b) in a green spotlight
c) in a blue spotlight?

White light from light bulbs or fluorescent tubes is different to normal daylight. Artificial light contains a slightly different mix of colours. This is why clothes you buy sometimes look different when you take them out of the shop.

You should know...

● **How to make coloured light.**

● **Why objects can look different in different coloured light.**

How does sound travel?

Sound is a form of energy. Being able to hear sound is one of our most important senses. Some of the sounds you hear are loud and some are soft. This is the **intensity** of the sound. Sounds can also be high or low. This is the **pitch** of the sound.

1 Look at the photograph of the funfair and list all the sounds that you might hear.

2 Choose examples from your list in question 1 to show high, low, soft and loud sounds.

3 Make a list of sound words such as bang, thump, scream, shriek.

How would you make different sounds using these items?
- How would you describe the sounds?

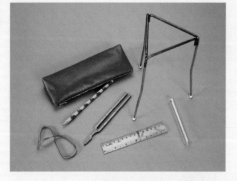

Sounds are made by something moving backwards and forwards. This is called **vibrating**. When you speak, vocal cords in your throat **vibrate**. When you play a guitar the strings vibrate to produce the sound.

The vibrating road drill makes a loud noise.

Vibrations of the cone of this loudspeaker cause the sand to jump.

A tuning fork is used to help musicians find a note. The fork is tapped lightly on something and the two prongs then vibrate to make a note.

A vibrating tuning fork can cause polystyrene balls to move.

4 What is a tuning fork?

5 What are vibrations?

6 What vibrates to produce a sound when a violin is played?

 The English trumpet player John Shore (c.1662–1752) invented the tuning fork in the year 1711. He played the solo trumpet at the coronation of George I in 1714 and he was a member of the king's orchestra for many years.

You can use a Slinky spring to help you to think about how sound moves. You create vibrations by pushing one end of the Slinky backwards and forwards. The vibrations travel as waves of energy along the Slinky.

If you push and pull on the end of a Slinky, the squashed parts travel along the Slinky.

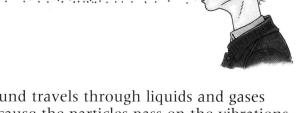

Sound waves travel in the same way. When sound travels through the air, the air particles squash up and move apart, just like the coils in the Slinky.

Sound travels through liquids and gases because the particles pass on the vibrations. Sounds travel fastest through solids, and slowest through gases.

7 How does sound travel from your mouth to someone's ear?

8 Why do you think that sound travels faster through solids than it does through gases? (*Hint*: Think about the arrangement of the particles in solids and gases.)

You should know...

- Sound is a form of energy.
- Sounds can be soft or loud, high or low.
- Sound travels because particles in solids, liquids, or gases pass on the vibrations.

How are different sounds made?

Different musical instruments make different sounds, because they are designed to make different sound **waves**.

 1 a) Make a list of eight musical instruments.
b) Next to each instrument, write down whether it is a stringed instrument, a wind instrument or a percussion instrument, and say what is vibrating to make the sound.

Sound patterns

You can use an **oscilloscope** to show a graph of sound waves. One complete wave is shown in red.

Frequency is the number of complete waves that pass a point each second. Frequency is measured in **hertz (Hz)**. If you listen to a sound with a frequency of 100 Hz, one hundred complete waves reach your ear every second. The **pitch** of the note (how high or low it sounds) depends on the frequency. High pitched sound waves have a high frequency, and low pitched sound waves have a low frequency.

one wave

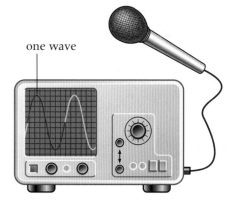

An oscilloscope.

The distance between the tops of two waves is called the **wavelength**.

A) The tops of these waves are far apart. They have a low **frequency**. These notes have a low **pitch**.

B) The tops of these waves are closer together, so they have a higher frequency. The note has a higher pitch.

C) The tops of these waves are very close together. They have a high frequency, and the note is high pitched.

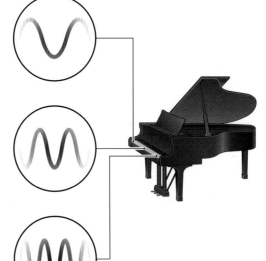

wavelength

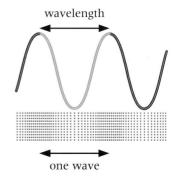

one wave

*The length of one wave is called the **wavelength**.*

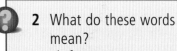

2 What do these words mean?
a) frequency
b) wavelength
c) pitch

P How would you investigate what affects the pitch of a note?
- How could you make sounds using the things in the photograph?
- How could you change the things to make higher or lower sounds?

Half the height of the wave is called the **amplitude**. The **loudness** of a sound depends on the amplitude. Louder notes have more energy and the wave has a bigger amplitude.

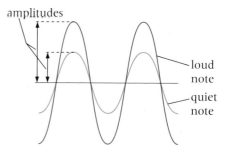

When the same note is played louder, the frequency stays the same but the amplitude becomes higher.

3 What do these words mean?
a) loudness   b) amplitude

4 What happens to a sound when:
a) the amplitude is increased
b) the frequency is increased?

5 a) Copy these waves.

b) Draw another set of waves with a higher frequency but the same amplitude.
c) Draw another set of waves with the same frequency as those in a) but with a higher amplitude.

6 Low pitched instruments have longer strings or tubes. Which violinist is making the higher pitched note?

X   Y

7 Copy this sentence and fill in the gaps.
The frequency of a certain sound wave is 250 _____ which tells us that _____ complete sound waves pass every _____ .

This relief from the Royal Palace at Nineveh, made in 900 BC, shows that musical instruments were in use nearly 3000 years ago. These were similar to those used today.

You should know...
- The meanings of the words amplitude, pitch and frequency.
- Frequency is measured in hertz (Hz).

Sound travelling light

What are the similarities and differences between sound and light?

Sound must have something to go through. It cannot travel through a **vacuum**. Sound travels by vibrations so it needs something to vibrate.

Sound travels through solids like doors, floors and walls.

Sound travels through liquids. Dolphins communicate by making high pitched sounds.

1 List three things that sound can travel through.

2 Why can't sound travel through space?

Sound travels through gases.

Sound cannot travel through a **vacuum** so you would not hear the spaceship exploding.

The British scientist Francis Hauksbee (1666–1713) experimented with a clock in a vacuum to prove that sound needs something to travel through.

An electric bell in a vacuum. Electric bells had not been invented in Hauksbee's day.

P How would you find out which substances sound travels through best? Would sound travel best through:
- the bench (solid)
- the water (liquid)
- or air (a gas)?

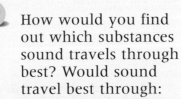

A L I E N

In space no one can hear you scream.

Sound travels through air at about 330 metres per second. Light travels about a million times faster.

The energy in a sound wave is passed through a material by particles vibrating. When one vibrating particle touches another, the vibrations are passed on.

Particles in solid materials are densely packed together. Particles are much less closely spaced in liquids and gases. Particles in gases are far apart and can move about freely. Sound travels fastest in solids because vibrations can be passed along very quickly by the particles which are all touching one another.

Material	Speed of sound (m/s)
Steel	6000
Aluminium	5100
Concrete	5000
Iron	5000
Glass	4500
Copper	3700
Brick	3000
Salt water	1560
Water	1500
Mercury	1450
Ethanol	1200
Air	330
Oxygen	316
Carbon dioxide	260

Newton's cradle can be used to model how energy can pass from one particle to another. When the first ball is released it hits the next ball and the vibrations pass along so that the last ball swings away.

3 Look at the photograph on the left-hand side of page 144. Why can the bell still be heard when there is no air inside the jar?

4 a) Copy the table of materials above and add a third column. In this column label each material, as solid, liquid or gas.
   b) What do you notice about the speed of sound through the different types of material?

5 The underwater explorer, Jacques Cousteau, once described the sea as the silent world. Do you think this is true? Give a reason for your answer.

6 Why can people see this train before they hear it?

7 Why would you be able to hear this train before it came around the bend?

Moving trains make the tracks vibrate.

You should know...

● **How the vibrations that make sounds travel through a medium.**

● **That sound cannot travel through a vacuum.**

● **That sound travels at different speeds through different types of material.**

● **How to use the particle model to explain how sound travels.**

How do we hear sounds?

Your ears change sound energy into electrical signals which are sent to your brain.

Vibrating sound waves travel through the air and into the ear, making the **eardrum** vibrate. The vibrations travel through the ear, passing from one material to another. When they reach the **cochlea** (pronounced '*cok-lee-a*') they are changed into electrical signals called **impulses** which travel down a nerve to the brain. When the impulses reach the brain we hear the sound.

1 What energy changes happen in your ears?

2 Which part of the ear:
a) detects the sound waves
b) sends messages to the brain
c) passes the vibrations from the eardrum to the cochlea?

3 a) List the parts of the ear and the jobs that they do.
b) Use this information to make a flow chart to show how sounds are heard.

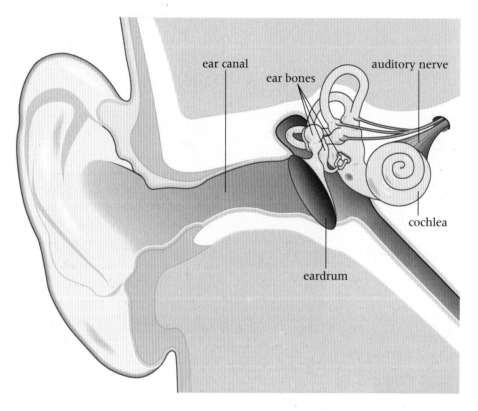

ear canal

ear bones

auditory nerve

cochlea

eardrum

Many animals have a much wider range of hearing than we do. Dogs can hear whistles we cannot hear. Dolphins and whales can communicate over long distances in the sea using very high-pitched clicks. Bats use their hearing like a radar for hunting prey and avoiding obstacles.

How would you find out whether everyone can hear the same sounds?
- You could use a signal generator and a loudspeaker to find out the highest and lowest sound you can hear.
- Can everyone else in the class hear the same sounds?

Ear damage

The ear is very delicate. It contains thin membranes (thin layers of cells) and tiny bones which are easily damaged.

- The ear can get blocked by wax, causing temporary deafness because the eardrum cannot vibrate. A doctor can wash out the wax and cure the deafness.
- Accidents or a loud bang can damage the eardrum. This may repair itself.
- The middle ear can get infected. Ear infections can be treated by antibiotics.
- As people get older the tiny bones in their ears sometimes fuse together. This prevents the vibrations from becoming bigger and causes hearing loss.
- Sometimes the nerve cells in the cochlea do not work as well when you get older so the messages are not sent to the brain.
- The cochlea can be affected by loud noise. People suffer hearing loss due to constant loud noise from nightclubs or wearing personal stereos that are too loud. There is no cure for this.

This man is having wax removed from his ears.

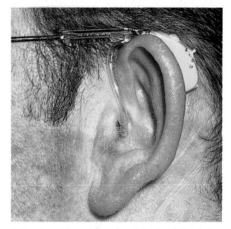

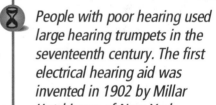
A hearing aid amplifies sound (makes it louder) and can be used to correct partial deafness. Someone with partial deafness can still hear a limited range of sounds.

The noise in nightclubs can damage your ears.

People working in noisy places wear ear protection.

4 Name three ways in which the ear can be damaged.

5 What is partial deafness and how can it be improved?

6 Design a poster to explain how people can avoid damaging their ears.

People with poor hearing used large hearing trumpets in the seventeenth century. The first electrical hearing aid was invented in 1902 by Millar Hutchinson of New York.

You should know...

- **How vibrations travel through the ear.**
- **That the ear changes sound energy into electrical signals called impulses which are sent to the brain.**
- **That some animals detect sounds that humans cannot hear.**
- **Some causes of hearing loss.**

What is noise?

Sometimes the sounds you hear can be very annoying. Sound can damage your ears if it is too loud or goes on for too long. Unpleasant sound is often called **noise**.

We can measure how loud a sound is by using a **sound intensity meter**. This is an instrument which measures the loudness of a sound in **decibels** (**dB**).

The **threshold of hearing** is the quietest sound we can hear. We call this 0 dB. The loudness of a road drill is 90 dB. This is the top limit of acceptable noise by law. A noisy factory can be louder than this. If you dance by the speakers in a nightclub you can hear sounds louder than 90 dB. Sound starts to become painful at about 80 dB and the eardrum breaks at 180 dB.

1 a) What is the instrument which measures noise levels called?
   b) What units do we use for noise levels?

At takeoff the sound intensity is 140 dB.

! *In November 1999, France brought out a law which limited the noise levels of personal stereos. From the year 2000 no personal stereos can be played louder than 100 decibels.*

2 What is the threshold of hearing?

3 What is the top limit of acceptable noise?

4 Make a list of jobs which have a high level of noise.

Soundproofing

Houses near to an airport usually have double-glazed windows. Most of the air has been taken out from between the layers of glass. This makes it more difficult for sound to travel through, as there are fewer particles to pass on the vibrations.

This factory is very noisy. The workers have to wear special ear protectors to stop their ears being damaged. This engineer is measuring the sound levels.

Noise can be reduced by soft things like carpets and curtains. The soft materials absorb some of the energy of the sound.

Noise can be a nuisance. How could you design a box that would stop the sound of a small item, such as a mobile phone or radio, from escaping?

?

5 How does double glazing cut down noise?

6 How can carpets and curtains reduce the noise in a room?

You should know...

● The loudness of a sound is measured in decibels by a sound intensity meter.

● Noise can be reduced by double glazing or soft materials.

149

How can echoes be used?

Like light, sound can be **reflected**. A reflected sound is called an **echo**. You can often hear echoes near mountains or in large caves. This is because sound is reflected by large solid objects such as walls, cliffs or mountains.

The greater horseshoe bat uses sound at 82 kHz to find its prey.

Bats are flying mammals that are nocturnal (come out at night). Many of them use echoes to avoid obstacles and catch insects. They send out very high pitched squeaks which we can't hear. The echoes of the squeaks tell the bat if something is in the way. Humans cannot usually hear the squeaks, because they are too high pitched for our ears to detect. Sounds that are too high for humans to hear are called **ultrasound**.

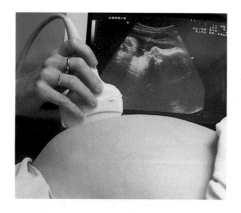

Ultrasound can be used to check on the progress of an unborn baby. A machine called an ultrasound transmitter is passed over the mother's body. Different parts of the body send back different echoes. These reflections of the sounds are processed by a computer and an image is displayed on a screen. Ultrasound is much safer for a mother and her baby than an X-ray, which could damage cells.

Submarines use **sonar** equipment to find where other ships are. A pulse of sound (a 'ping') is sent out from the submarine. The sound is reflected off objects and the echo of the sound returns to the submarine. The time taken for the echo to return is measured and the distance is calculated by a computer. Fishing boats can use a similar system to help them to find shoals of fish.

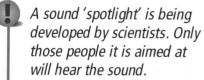

! *A sound 'spotlight' is being developed by scientists. Only those people it is aimed at will hear the sound.*

1 What is ultrasound?

2 How do many bats 'see' in the dark?

3 a) What is an ultrasound transmitter used for?
   b) Why is it safer than X-rays?

4 How is sound useful in:
   a) submarines
   b) fishing boats?

5 The highest frequency sound we can hear is about 20 000 Hz. Explain what this means.

How does the speed of sound vary?

The speed of sound in air depends on the temperature of the air. It travels faster in warm air than in cool air. The speed of sound is different in different materials.

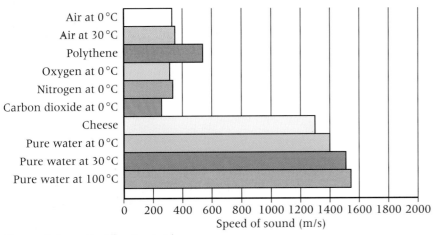

The speed of sound in different materials.

The sound barrier

In the Second World War, aircraft were built that could fly faster and faster. Strange things happened when they flew close to the speed of sound. The planes began to shake rapidly. For a while it was thought that it was not possible to fly faster than the speed of sound and the term **sound barrier** was used.

Scientists looked for ways to reduce the vibrations caused by high speeds. Soon planes were more pointed and streamlined, with swept back wings. These planes could overcome the problems of violent shaking.

 How could you use the idea of echoes to measure the speed of sound?
- You could use a metre rule or a long tape measure, a stop watch and a wall.
- The equation for speed is:

$$\text{speed} = \frac{\text{distance travelled}}{\text{time taken}}$$

A shock wave forms around the aircraft when it goes faster than the speed of sound.

 The first aircraft to go faster than the speed of sound was the American Bell X-1 rocket plane flown by Captain Chuck Yeager on October 14th 1947.

1 a) Where in the world do you think the speed of sound is fastest?
   b) Explain your answer.

2 Look at the bar chart at the top of this page.
   a) Explain the order of the speed of sound in the different materials in terms of particles.
   b) Which one seems to be the odd one out?
   c) On a hot day (30 °C) how far does sound travel in 10 seconds?

3 a) What is the sound barrier?
   b) How do modern aircraft cope with the sound barrier?

Glossary

Pronunciation note: A capital 'O' is said as in 'so'

abrasion (*ab-bray-shun*)	When something is worn away by particles.
absolute scale (temperature)	A temperature scale starting at 0 Kelvin (–273 °C).
absolute zero	The temperature at which atoms stop vibrating. 0 K or –273 °C.
absorb (in biology)	To take in, e.g. when soluble substances pass through the wall of the small intestine and into the blood.
absorb (in physics)	To take in, e.g. when light is taken up by a material and does not reflect it.
adaptation (*add-app-tay-shun*)	The features of an organism that allow it to live in its environment.
adapted	When the features of an organism help it to survive in a habitat, it is adapted to that habitat.
aerobic (*air-rO-bick*)	With air.
aerobic respiration (*air-rO-bick*)	Process that releases energy from digested food. Needs oxygen from the air. Carbon dioxide is produced as a waste gas.
AIDS	A disease caused by the HIV virus which leads to the weakening of the immune system. Short for **a**cquired **i**mmuno**d**eficiency **s**yndrome.
air sacs	Groups of alveoli in the lungs where oxygen comes out of the air and goes into the blood. Carbon dioxide is also transferred from the blood to the air in these.
alloy	A mixture of different metals.
alveoli (*al-vee-O-lee*)	Pockets in the lungs where oxygen comes out of the air and goes into the blood. Carbon dioxide is also transferred from the blood to the air in the alveoli. Singular = alveolus.
amino acids (*am-mee-no ass-id*)	The building blocks of proteins. When proteins are digested they are broken down to form amino acids.
amphibian	Vertebrate with moist skin, e.g. frog.
amplitude	Half the height of a wave.
amylase	Enzyme that breaks starch down into sugar.
anaerobic (*an-air-rO-bick*)	Without air.
anaerobic respiration (*an-air-rO-bick*)	A type of respiration that does not need oxygen. In humans, it produces lactic acid. In yeast it produces ethanol (alcohol).
angle of incidence (*in-sid-dense*)	The angle between the normal and a ray of light hitting a mirror or object.
angle of reflection	The angle between the normal and a ray of light leaving a mirror.
angle of refraction	Angle between the light ray and the normal as it passes through an interface.
animal kingdom	The group of organisms that contains all vertebrates and invertebrates.
antibiotic (*ant-ee-by-ot-tick*)	Medicine that can kill bacteria but not viruses.
antibody	Small chemical made by some white blood cells. They attach to microbes and help to destroy them.
antiseptic	Weak disinfectant that is safe to use on human skin.
anus	The opening at the end of the gut.
appendix	Small tube branching off the large intestine. It has no function in humans.
armature	The iron part of a relay that moves when electricity is flowing in the solenoid.
artery	Blood vessel that carries blood away from the heart.
arthropod (*arth-row-pod*)	Invertebrate that has jointed legs, e.g. fly, spider.
atom	The smallest part of an element.
attract	Two things pull towards each other.

bacterium	A type of microbe bigger than viruses. Plural = bacteria.
balanced diet	Eating a variety of foods to provide all the things the body needs.
bar magnet	A straight magnet, shaped like a bar.
basalt (*bas-salt*)	Igneous rock with very small crystals.
bauxite	Aluminium ore.
bile	Liquid produced by the liver used to emulsify fats in the small intestine.
bird	Vertebrate with feathers, e.g. eagle.
blood	Liquid made out of cells and plasma that flows around the body carrying various substances which are either made by or needed by the body.
blood vessel	Tube in which blood flows. There are capillaries, veins and arteries.
blue	One of the three primary colours of light.
boiling point	When a liquid is at its boiling point it is as hot as it can get. It is evaporating as fast as it can.
bond	Force holding atoms together.
breathing	Moving muscles in order to make air flow into and out of the lungs.
breathing rate	The number of times you breathe in one minute.
breathing system	Set of organs that allows air to be taken into and out of the body (lungs, windpipe, diaphragm).
bronchus (*bron-kus*)	Tube in the lungs that connects the windpipe to the air sac. Plural = bronchi.
budding	The way yeast cells divide. A new small cell (a bud) starts t grow out from another cell.
burning	When a chemical reacts with oxygen and releases energy i the form of heat.
calcium	A metal which reacts easily with water. Compounds contai this metal are important in our diets for strong teeth and b
camera	A box that lets light through a hole in one side to form an image.
capillaries (*cap-ill-arr-ees*)	The smallest blood vessels. Substances enter and leave the blood through the thin walls of capillaries.
carbohydrate (*car-bo-high-drate*)	Substance found in food that is used for energy.
carbon dioxide	A gas which will put out a lighted splint, and turn limewater milky. It is a product of respiration.
carbonate-rich	Something which contains a lot of compounds called carbonates.
carnivore	An animal that only eats other animals.
Celsius (*sell-see-us*)	Degrees Celsius – the units of temperature.
cementation	A process in which water flowing through the spaces between the grains of rock leaves mineral salts behind whi stick (cement) the rock pieces together.
cemented	Something that has been stuck together.
chalk	A soft white or grey sedimentary rock formed from the remains of microscopic organisms and so mainly made out calcium carbonate.
chamber	The heart contains four compartments called chambers.
chemical energy	The kind of energy stored in chemicals. Food, fuels and electrical cells all contain chemical energy.
chemical formula	A combination of symbols and numbers that shows how n atoms of different kinds are in a particular molecule.
chemical reaction	When new substances join.
chemical weathering	When rocks are broken up by chemical changes.

...romosome (...row-mow-sowm)	String like threads contained in the nucleus of a cell. Chromosomes contain DNA which contains the instructions for inherited variation.
...romatography (...row-mat-og-graph-ee)	Separating dissolved solids from one another. The solids are usually coloured.
...lia	Small hairs growing from some cells that can sweep things along.
...iated epithelial cell (...il-lee-ay-ted eppy-...eel-ee-al)	Cells in the trachea which have microscopic hairs (cilia) growing from them. They wave to move mucus up to the gullet to be swallowed.
...rculatory system	System containing the heart and blood vessels.
...assification	Placing things into groups according to their characteristics.
...ot	When the blood becomes solid. Makes a 'scab' when it is on the surface of the skin.
...al	A fossil fuel made from the remains of plants.
...balt (cO-balt)	A metal that is a magnetic material.
...chlea (cok-lee-a)	The part of the ear that changes vibrations into electrical impulses.
...eliac disease (...ee-lee-ack)	A disease in which the villi in the small intestine are destroyed.
...mbination reaction	When chemicals join to form new substances.
...mmunity (...m-mew-nit-ee)	All the plants and animals that live in a habitat.
...mpaction	When layers of sediment or rock are squashed by the weight of sediment above them.
...mpass	An instrument used to find direction. In a compass a needle swings around and points to magnetic north.
...mpete	All organisms need some of the same things and so each organism has to try to get these things before another organism does. For example, plants compete with one another for light.
...mpetition (...m-pet-tish-un)	Organisms compete with each other for food, light and space in a habitat.
...mpound	Substance that can be split up into simpler substances.
...ndense	When a gas turns into a liquid.
...nduction (...n-duck-shun)	The way heat travels through solids.
...nductor	Material that lets energy flow through it easily.
...nifer	Plant with needle shaped leaves. Reproduces using seeds found in cones.
...nstipation (...n-stip-ay-shun)	When the intestines get blocked up.
...nstructive plate margin	An area where two tectonic plates are moving apart. As magma fills up the gap between the plates new rock is formed.
...nsumer	An organism that has to eat other organisms to stay alive. Animals are consumers.
...ntract	Get smaller.
...nvection	The transfer of heat in fluids.
...nvection current	A current created by heat causing changes in the density of a fluid.
...quina	A soft, white type of limestone made from large shell fragments.
...re	A solid bar inside an electromagnet, usually made of iron. Also the middle of the Earth.
...st	The solid rocks covering the surface of the Earth.
...stals (kris-tals)	A mineral with a regular shape.
...icle (cute-ick-al)	Layer of cells on leaves that is waterproof.
...an (sy-ann)	Secondary colour made by mixing green and blue light. A bit like turquoise.
...cibel	Unit for measuring the loudness of a sound (dB).
...compose	Break down.

degree Celsius (°C) (sell-see-us)	The units for measuring temperature.
deposits	When moving water drops the rock fragments or grains it has been carrying.
destructive plate margin	An area where two tectonic plates are moving **towards** each other. One plate is forced down below the other.
diabetes (dye-a-beet-ees)	Disease when the pancreas does not produce enough insulin to control the levels of glucose in the blood.
diagnosis	Identifying what disease a person has from looking at the symptoms the person has.
diaphragm (dye-a-fram)	Sheet of muscle underneath the lungs. It helps to work the lungs.
diet	The food a person eats.
diffusion (dif-you-shun)	The natural movement of particles from a place where there are a lot of them to a place where there are fewer of them.
digestion (di-jes-jun)	Process that breaks down food into soluble substances in our bodies.
digestive juice	A liquid containing enzymes that break down food.
digestive system	The group of organs that carries out digestion.
disease	When some processes that happen in the body do not work in the way that they should.
disinfectant	Strong chemical used to kill microbes.
dispersion	The separating of the colours in light, for example when white light passes through a prism.
distillation	The process of separating a liquid from a solution by evaporating the liquid and then condensing it.
distribution (diss-trib-you-shun)	The places where an organism can be found in a habitat.
DNA	The substance that chromosomes are made out of.
eardrum	Thin membrane inside the ear which vibrates when sound reaches it.
echinoderm (ek-eye-no-derm)	Invertebrate that has a body in five parts, e.g. starfish.
echo (eck-O)	Sound which is reflected back from something solid.
ecologist	A person who studies the environment.
egestion (ee-jes-jun)	When faeces are pushed out of the anus.
electrical conductor	Something which allows electricity to flow through it easily.
electrolysis	Splitting up a chemical using electricity.
electromagnet	A coil of wire with electricity flowing in it. An electromagnet has a magnetic field like a bar magnet.
element	A substance that cannot be split up into anything simpler by chemical means.
emit (ee-mit)	To give out energy.
emulsion	Two liquids mixed together; one forming small blobs in the other.
endangered	A species which is at risk from becoming extinct.
energy	Something that is needed to make things happen.
engulf	When a white blood cell completely surrounds a microbe and destroys it, it is said to engulf the microbe.
environment	The surroundings of an organism.
environmental variation	Differences between organisms caused by environmental factors.
enzyme (en-zeye-m)	A chemical that can break up large molecules.
erosion (er-O-shun)	The movement of loose and weathered rock.
essential amino acid (amm-ee-no)	Amino acid that the body needs to stay healthy.
estimate	Provide a rough idea about the numbers of something or the size of something.
ethanol	Often just called 'alcohol'. Produced by yeast when they ferment sugar.
evaporate	When a liquid turns into a gas.

evidence	Information that helps to prove that an idea is correct.
excrete (ecks-creet)	The process of getting rid of waste substances that have been made in the body by chemical reactions.
exhale	Breathe out.
exhaled air	Air that is breathed out.
exoskeleton (ex-O-skel-e-ton)	Thick outer covering found in arthropods.
expand	Get bigger.
extinct	A species that no longer exists.
faeces (fee-sees)	Waste food material that comes out of the anus.
Fahrenheit (fa-ren-hite)	A temperature scale that is still used in some parts of the world. On this scale water freezes at 32 °F and boils at 212 °F.
fat	Substance found in food that is stored to be used for energy in the future. It also helps to keep heat in our bodies.
feeding	Putting food into your mouth. Also called ingestion.
fermentation	The type of anaerobic respiration carried out by yeast. It produces carbon dioxide and ethanol.
fern	Plant that has many small waterproof leaves. Reproduces using spores.
fever (fee-ver)	A high body temperature.
fibre (feye-ber)	Substance found in food which cannot be digested. It helps to keep our intestines clean.
filter (in physics)	Something which only lets certain colours of light through and absorbs the rest.
fish	Vertebrate with wet scales, e.g. salmon.
flagellum (flaj-ell-um)	Tail on, for example, a bacterium. Plural = flagellae.
flowering plant	Plant with large, flat leaves. Reproduces using seeds found in fruits. Fruits and seeds form inside flowers.
fluid	A gas or a liquid.
food chain	A way of showing what eats what in a habitat.
food web	Many food chains linked together.
formula	Symbols and numbers that tell you how many atoms of different kinds there are in a molecule.
fossil	Any sign of past life that has been preserved in a rock.
fractional distillation	A way of separating two liquids with different boiling points, e.g. alcohol and water.
fractionating column (frack-shon-ate-ing)	A large tower used to separate the different liquids in crude oil.
freeze-thaw	A kind of weathering that happens when water gets into a crack in a rock and freezes. The freezing water expands and makes the crack bigger.
freezing point	The temperature at which a liquid turns into a solid.
frequency	The number of waves each second.
fuel	A chemical which can release energy when it reacts.
fungus	A type of organism that does not make its own food. It feeds off dead plants and animals. Plural = fungi.
gas	Something made of particles that are very spread out and are not attached to each other. It does not have a fixed shape or volume and is easy to squash.
gas exchange	Process where oxygen is taken into the lungs and carbon dioxide is passed out of the lungs as a waste product of respiration. It happens in the alveoli.
gene (jeen)	A length of DNA that controls one inherited feature of an organism.
gill	A series of flaps of tissue with a good blood supply just behind the head of an organism which is used to take oxygen out of water. Fish have gills.
global warming	The process of the Earth's atmosphere warming up. It is partly caused by an increase in carbon dioxide in the air.
glucose	A type of sugar.
grain	Small pieces of minerals.
granite (gran-it)	Igneous rock made from large crystals.

green	One of the three primary colours of light.
gullet	Tube that goes from the mouth to the stomach but proper called the oesophagus.
gut	All the organs of the digestive system apart from the mou
habitat	The place an organism lives in, e.g. woodland.
heart	Organ that pumps blood around the body.
heart attack	When the heart stops pumping.
heart chambers	The heart contains four compartments called chambers.
heart disease	Disease caused by narrowing of the arteries carrying bloo to the muscles of the heart. So the heart muscles do not receive enough oxygen.
heat conductor	Something which allows heat to flow through it easily.
heat energy	The hotter something is, the more heat energy it has.
heat insulator	Something which does not allow heat to flow through it easily.
herbivore	An animal that only eats plants.
hertz	Unit of frequency (Hz). 1 hertz means one wave per seco
high melting point	Something with a high melting point has to be at a very h temperature before it melts. It is a solid at room temperatu
HIV	A virus that causes AIDS. Stands for human immunodeficiency virus.
HIV positive	Someone who has HIV in their body is described as being HIV positive.
humidity	The amount of water vapour in the air.
humus (huw-mus)	Rotting organisms (especially leaves) which form part of the soil.
hydrogencarbonate indicator	An indicator that can be used to show how much carbon dioxide there is in something.
igneous rock (igg-nee-us)	Rock formed when magma or lava cools down and freeze (solidifies).
image	A picture which forms in a mirror or on a screen, or is m. by lenses.
immune (imm-you'n)	If you cannot get a disease you are said to be immune to
immunisation (imm-you'n-eyes-ay-shun)	Making people immune to diseases.
impulse	Electrical signal carried by a nerve cell.
incident ray	Light ray hitting a mirror.
infect	When a microbe gets into your body you are infected by
infectious (in-feck-shus)	A disease that can be spread from person to person or fro animal to person is infectious.
infrared radiation	A type of wave in the electromagnetic spectrum.
ingestion (in-jes-jun)	Putting food into your mouth.
inhale	Breathe in.
inhaled air	Air that is breathed in.
insoluble (in-sol-you-bull)	Something that does not dissolve.
insulator	A substance which does not allow energy to flow.
insulin (in-syou-lin)	A hormone produced by the pancreas that lowers the lev of glucose in the blood.
intensity	The strength or amount of some things is described in ter of intensity. For example, a bright light has a greater inte than a dim light.
interface	Boundary between substances.
interlocking	Fitting together, like a jigsaw puzzle.
invertebrate (in-vert-eb-rate)	Animal with no backbone.
iron	A metal that is a magnetic material.
iron filings (feye-lings)	Tiny pieces of iron.
irreversible change	Permanent change.
joule (J)	The unit for measuring energy.
Kelvin	A temperature scale often used by scientists. 0 K is absolu zero (−273 °C).

ojoule (kill-o-jool)	Unit of energy used on food packets (kJ). There are 1000 joules in 1 kJ.
ngdom	Largest groups that living things are sorted into. The two biggest are the plant kingdom and the animal kingdom.
rge intestine	Organ that takes water out of waste food.
ser (lays-er)	Something which produces a narrow beam of light.
va (larv-er)	Molten rock that flows from volcanoes.
mestone	A sedimentary rock, made mainly of calcium carbonate, which is formed from the shells of dead sea animals.
newater	A chemical that goes cloudy when carbon dioxide is bubbled through it.
miting factor	Something that stops a population growing.
uid	Something made of particles that are fairly close together, but are attached weakly so that they can move past each other. It has a fixed volume but not a fixed shape.
er	An organ in the body. It has a number of functions including making bile.
am	A good soil containing both clay and sand particles.
udness	How loud a sound is; the volume of a sound.
udspeaker	A paper cone moved by a magnet and an electromagnet. It converts electrical signals into sound.
w boiling point	Something with a low boiling point will turn into a gas at a relatively low temperature. It can be a solid, liquid or gas at room temperature.
w melting point	Something with a low melting point turns into a liquid at a relatively low temperature. It can be a solid, liquid or gas at room temperature.
minous source	Object which creates light.
genta (maj-ent-a)	A purplish secondary colour made by mixing red and blue light.
glev	Trains that use electromagnets to make them float (or levitate) above the tracks and move along are called maglev trains.
gma	Molten rock beneath the surface of the Earth.
gnet	Something that can attract magnetic materials.
gnetic	Material that is attracted to a magnet.
gnetic field	The space around a magnet where it can affect magnetic materials or other magnets.
gnetic material	Material that is attracted to a magnet; iron, cobalt, nickel and steel are all magnetic materials.
gnetic north	The direction to which the magnetic needle of a compass points. (This is different to the north direction marked on maps.)
gnetism	A non-contact force.
ke and break switch	The switch in an electric bell that opens and closes because of an electromagnet breaking the circuit every time it is switched on.
tase	An enzyme that turns maltose into glucose.
tose	A type of sugar (two glucose molecules joined together).
mmal	Vertebrate with hair and produces milk, e.g. human.
ntle	The part of the Earth below the crust where rocks are molten (in liquid form).
ble	Metamorphic rock formed from limestone.
dicine (med-iss-in)	A drug that helps the body to ease the symptoms of a disease or cure the disease.
dium	Any substance.
t	When a solid turns into a liquid.
ting point	The temperature at which a solid turns into a liquid.
al	A type of substance that is shiny, conducts heat and electricity well, and has high melting and boiling points.
amorphic (t-a-mor-fik)	A word meaning 'changed'.

metamorphic rock (met-a-mor-fik)	Rock that has been formed by changing igneous or sedimentary rocks.
microbe	Short for micro-organism.
micro-organism	A very small living thing.
mineral	Short for 'mineral salt'. The chemical compounds found in rocks and soil. Humans and plants need minerals for growth.
mineral salt	See mineral.
mixture	Two or more different kinds of particles that are not joined to each other.
model	A scientific way of thinking about how things happen.
molar	Grinding tooth at the back of the mouth.
molecule	Two or more atoms joined together.
mollusc	Invertebrate that crawls on a fleshy pad, e.g. snail.
moss	Plant with no roots and no xylem and many thin leaves. Reproduces using spores.
mucus (mew-cus)	Sticky substance used to trap microbes and dust. Found in the nose and trachea.
mudstone	Sedimentary rock made from mud.
natural defences	Your body's way of trying to keep microbes out (e.g. skin) or killing them if they get inside you (e.g. stomach acid).
natural gas	Fossil fuel formed from the remains of dead plants and animals that lived in the sea.
neutralise	When an acid is added to a base (or alkali) and a neutral substance is produced.
nickel	A metal that is a magnetic material.
noise	Unpleasant sound.
non-metal	A substance that is not a metal. Non-metals are not shiny, and do not conduct heat and electricity well.
normal (in physics)	Imaginary line at right angles to a mirror.
north magnetic pole	The place on the Earth where compasses point. It is not in the same place as the North Pole marked on maps.
north pole	One end of a magnet. This end points north if the magnet can move.
north-seeking pole	The end of a magnet that points north if the magnet can move freely. Often just called the north pole.
nutrients (new-tree-ents)	Substances needed in the diet to keep you healthy (carbohydrates, fats, proteins, vitamins and minerals).
nutrition information (new-trish-un)	Information found on food packets which tells you what it contains.
observation	Looking carefully at things and recording what you see or measure.
oil	Fossil fuel formed from the remains of dead plants and animals that lived in the sea.
omnivore	An animal that eats both plants and other animals.
oolite (oo-lite)	A type of limestone formed when water evaporates and leaves calcium carbonate behind.
opaque (O-pake)	Material which does not let light through.
optical fibre (feye-ber)	Made of glass. Light travels down optical fibres because it is reflected from the inside surface of the fibre.
organism	A living thing.
oscilloscope (oss-sill-O-scope)	Instrument which shows a picture of a wave on a screen.
oxide	A compound that includes oxygen.
oxygen	A gas which will make a lighted splint burn brighter, or re-light a glowing splint.
oxygen debt (det)	Amount of oxygen that is needed to break down the lactic acid produced by anaerobic respiration.
pancreas (pank-cree-as)	An organ that produces digestive enzymes and hormones.
particles	Tiny things that everything is made of.
pasteurisation (pas-ter-eyes-ay-shun)	Milk is heated up to 70 °C for about 15 seconds which is enough to kill the most harmful bacteria in it.
Periodic Table (peer-ee-od-ick)	Table that shows all the elements.

permanent magnet	A magnet that keeps its magnetism; it does not depend on electricity.
persistent chemical	A chemical that does not get broken down in nature very quickly. It stays around for a long time.
pest	Organism that damages crops.
pesticide (pest-iss-ide)	Chemical that kills pests.
phenylketonuria (phee-nile-key-tO-new-ree-a)	A disease where the body cannot break down an amino acid called phenylalanine.
phloem	Tissues which carry substances like glucose around a plant.
photosynthesis (foto-sinth-e-sis)	Process that plants used to make their own food. It needs light to work. Carbon dioxide and water are the reactants. Food (a sugar called glucose) and oxygen are the products.
physical change (fizz-ick-al)	A change where no new substances are formed.
physical environmental factor	Something in an environment that can change a feature of an organism.
physical weathering	When rocks are broken up by physical changes.
pinhole camera	Something which forms an image of an object when light rays travel through a tiny hole in the front.
pitch	How high or low a note sounds.
pitfall trap	Sampling method used to collect small animals that live on the ground.
plane mirror	Smooth, flat mirror.
plant kingdom	Group of organisms that are able to produce their own food and have specialised cells.
plasma	Part of the blood; a liquid that surrounds the blood cells.
plate	The Earth's crust is made of a series of tectonic plates.
plate tectonics	The theory that the Earth's crust is made of a series of moving plates.
plotting compass	Small compass used for finding the direction of a magnetic field.
pond dipping	Sampling method used to collect organisms from ponds.
pooter	A small container connected to two tubes. Used to catch tiny animals.
population	The numbers of a certain organism found in a certain area.
porous (poor-us)	Rocks that can soak up water (e.g. sandstone).
potassium	Soft, shiny, reactive, silver-coloured metal.
precipitate (pres-sip-it-tate)	Insoluble solid produced by mixing two solutions.
predator	An animal that catches and eats other animals.
predict	When you have an idea about what will happen when you change something.
pressure	The force caused by particles hitting a certain area.
prey (pray)	An animal that is caught and eaten by another animal.
primary colours (pry-marr-ee)	The three main colours which can make white light (red, green and blue).
primary consumer	The first animal in a food chain.
prism	Block of glass which is usually triangular.
producer	Organism that is able to make its own food.
product	New chemical formed in a chemical reaction.
properties	Ways of describing a substance.
protein	Substance found in food that is needed for growth and repair.
protein coat	The outer covering of a virus particle is made of protein and so is called a protein coat.
pulse	The feel of your blood being pumped.
pulse rate	The number of times you can feel your blood being pumped in one minute.
pupil	Transparent part in the centre of the eye where light passes through.
pure	A substance that does not have anything else in it.
pyramid of numbers	Way of showing the numbers of organisms in a food chain.

quadrat	A square frame, thrown randomly on the ground, which used to sample the plants in an area.
quartzite	A metamorphic rock formed from sandstone.
radiation	The transfer of heat energy by electromagnetic waves.
rainbow	Spectrum formed when small drops of water in the air re light.
raw materials	Substances used to make other substances out of.
ray	A beam of light usually shown on diagrams as a straight
ray diagram	A diagram showing the paths of light rays.
reactant	Chemical that is used up in a chemical reaction.
rectum	Organ that stores faeces before they are egested through the anus.
red	One of the three primary colours of light.
red blood cells	Cells in the blood that carry oxygen.
reed switch	Switch made from two thin pieces of metal, which closes when it is in a magnetic field.
reflect	Light bounces back from a surface instead of passing through it.
reflected ray	The ray of light bouncing off a mirror.
refraction	Change in direction when light goes from one transparer material to another.
relay	A switch that is turned on and off by electricity.
repel	Push away.
replicate	Viruses cannot reproduce on their own. They use the ce which they have infected to help them make new copies the virus. We say that the virus particles replicate.
replication	The process that happens when a cell makes new copies virus.
reproduce	To produce a new organism that is like its parents.
reptile	Vertebrate with dry scales, e.g. snake.
resistant	Bacteria that are not affected by an antibiotic are said to resistant to it.
respiration (ress-per-ay-shun)	Process that uses up a sugar (glucose) and oxygen to rel energy from food. Carbon dioxide is produced as a wast
retina	Layer at the back of the eye which changes light energy electrical energy.
reversible change	A change in which what you end up with can easily be turned back into what you started with.
rock cycle	All the processes which form igneous, sedimentary and metamorphic rocks, linked together.
rock fragments	Small pieces of rock.
root	Plant organ used to take water out of the soil.
saliva (sall-eye-va)	Digestive juice containing amylase, an enzyme that brea down starch into sugar.
salivary gland	Small pouch in the mouth that produces saliva.
salts	Chemicals from rocks that have dissolved in water.
sample	A small part taken from a much larger thing. To sample something means to look at what a small par something contains.
sandstone	A sedimentary rock formed from grains of sand cement together.
scab	A dry blood clot on the surface of the skin.
scatter	When light rays bounce off something in all directions.
secondary colour (seck-on-dree)	Colour made when two primary colours overlap.
secondary consumer	The second animal in a food chain.
sediment	Rock grains and fragments dropped on the bottom of a lake or sea.
sedimentary rock	Rock formed from layers of sediment; it may contain fo
seeds	Grow into new plants. Made by conifers and flowering
shadow	Place where light cannot get to, because an opaque obj stopping the light.

ale	A sedimentary rock.
iny	Reflects light well.
ate	Metamorphic rock made from very small crystals; formed from mudstone.
nall intestine	Organ where most digestion happens. The soluble substances produced by digestion are absorbed into the body here.
dium chloride (w-dee-um **klor**-ide)	Chemical name for common salt.
lenoid	A coil of wire.
lid	Something made of particles that are very close together and attached so that they cannot move past each other. It has a fixed shape and volume.
luble (**sol**-you-bull)	Something that dissolves.
vent	A liquid that can dissolve other substances.
nar (**sO**-nar)	A machine for finding the depth of the sea or for finding fish by sending sound waves and listening for the echoes.
und	Form of energy made by something vibrating.
und barrier	The speed of sound; people used to think that it would be impossible to travel faster than the speed of sound.
und intensity	The loudness of a sound.
und intensity meter	A meter which measures the loudness of a sound.
urce	An object which creates something.
uth pole	One end of a magnet.
uth-seeking pole	The end of a magnet that points south if the magnet can move freely. Often just called the south pole.
ectrum	The seven colours in white light.
ore	Very small part of a plant that can grow into a new plant. Made by mosses and ferns.
rch	A carbohydrate made from glucose molecules joined together. Plants use it as a store of energy.
el	An alloy made from iron and carbon; it is a magnetic material.
mach (**stum**-uck)	Organ containing strong acid which mixes food up and helps with digestion.
and of genes	A length of DNA that contains genes.
soil	The layer of soil that is beneath the soil on the surface (topsoil) but above the rock.
gar	A type of soluble carbohydrate.
phur	A yellow, non-metal element. Solid at room temperature.
eepnet	Sampling method used to collect small animals from long grass.
nbol	The letter or letters that represent an element.
nbol equation	A way of writing out what happens in a chemical reaction using the symbols that represent the substances involved.
nptoms	The effects that a disease has on your body.
lymphocyte (n-fow-site)	A type of white blood cell that helps to fight off infections.
nperature	How hot something is, measured in °C.
tiary consumer (rsh-ary)	The third *animal* in a food chain.
ture (rocks)	The sizes and shapes of the grains that make up a rock.
ory (**thear**-ree)	A scientific idea that can be tested.
rmal energy	Another name for heat energy.
eshold of hearing	The quietest sound that can be heard.

tissue	Group of cells of the same type all doing the same job.
tissue fluid	Liquid formed when plasma leaks out of capillaries carrying oxygen and dissolved food to cells.
top predator	The last *animal* in a food chain.
topsoil	The top layer of soil.
total internal reflection	When light is reflected inside a piece of glass or other transparent material.
toxic	Another word for poisonous.
trachea (track-**ee**-a)	Another name for the windpipe.
translucent (trans-**loo**-sent)	Material through which a glow of light can be seen.
transmit	To send along or pass through.
transparent	Material which light can travel through.
transport	Movement of rock grains and fragments by wind or water.
tree beating	Sampling method used to collect animals from trees and bushes.
Tullgren funnel	Sampling method used to collect small animals from samples of, e.g., leaves.
ultrasound	Sound that has a frequency too high for humans to hear.
uneven distribution	When a plant or animal is not found all over a habitat, only in certain places where the habitat is suitable.
vaccine (**vack**-seen)	A mixture containing microbes which normally cause disease, which have been treated so that they don't. Injected into people to make them immune.
vacuum	A completely empty space containing no particles.
vein (vane)	Blood vessel that carries blood towards the heart.
ventilation	The movement of air into and out of the lungs.
vertebrate (**vert**-eb-rate)	Animal with a backbone.
vibrate	Move backwards and forwards.
villi (**vill**-ee)	Small finger-like parts of the wall of the small intestine. They increase the surface area so that digested food is absorbed more quickly. Singular = villus.
virus	The smallest type of microbe. Many people think that they are not living because they do not carry out the seven life processes for themselves.
vitamin	Substance found in food that is needed in small quantities for health (e.g. vitamin C).
volcano	Landform where lava flows out of the Earth.
water	A compound which consists of molecules each containing two hydrogen atoms bonded to an oxygen atom. Also called hydrogen oxide.
wave	A way of transferring energy. Waves can be side to side or backwards and forwards movements.
wavelength	The distance between the start of a wave and its end.
weathered	Rocks that have been broken up by chemical, biological or physical processes.
white blood cell	A type of blood cell which helps to destroy microbes. They either engulf microbes or make antibodies.
white light	Normal daylight, or the light from light bulbs.
word equation	Way of writing out what happens in a chemical reaction.
xylem vessel (zy-lem)	Transports water through a plant.
yeast	A type of fungus with only one cell and therefore a microbe. Yeasts are bigger than bacteria.
yellow	Secondary colour made by mixing red and green light.

The Periodic Table

Key:

30		
Zn	— atomic number (30), atomic symbol (Zn)	
zinc	— name of element	
65	— mass number	

Legend: metal | semi metal | non-metal

gaps left for undiscovered elements

1	2	3	4	5	6	7	8	9	10	11	12	13	14	15	16	17	18
1 **H** hydrogen 1																	2 **He** helium 4
3 **Li** lithium 7	4 **Be** beryllium 9											5 **B** boron 11	6 **C** carbon 12	7 **N** nitrogen 14	8 **O** oxygen 16	9 **F** fluorine 19	10 **Ne** neon 20
11 **Na** sodium 23	12 **Mg** magnesium 24											13 **Al** aluminium 27	14 **Si** silicon 28	15 **P** phosphorus 31	16 **S** sulphur 32	17 **Cl** chlorine 35	18 **Ar** argon 40
19 **K** potassium 40	20 **Ca** calcium 40	21 **Sc** scandium 45	22 **Ti** titanium 48	23 **V** vanadium 51	24 **Cr** chromium 52	25 **Mn** manganese 55	26 **Fe** iron 56	27 **Co** cobalt 59	28 **Ni** nickel 59	29 **Cu** copper 64	30 **Zn** zinc 65	31 **Ga** gallium 70	32 **Ge** germanium 73	33 **As** arsenic 75	34 **Se** selenium 79	35 **Br** bromine 80	36 **Kr** krypton 84
37 **Rb** rubidium 85	38 **Sr** strontium 88	39 **Y** yttrium 89	40 **Zr** zirconium 91	41 **Nb** niobium 93	42 **Mo** molybdenum 96	43 **Tc** technetium 98	44 **Ru** ruthenium 101	45 **Rh** rhodium 103	46 **Pd** palladium 106	47 **Ag** silver 108	48 **Cd** cadmium 112	49 **In** indium 115	50 **Sn** tin 119	51 **Sb** antimony 122	52 **Te** tellurium 128	53 **I** iodine 127	54 **Xe** xenon 131
55 **Cs** caesium 133	56 **Ba** barium 137	57 **La** lanthanum 139	72 **Hf** hafnium 178	73 **Ta** tantalum 181	74 **W** tungsten 184	75 **Re** rhenium 186	76 **Os** osmium 190	77 **Ir** iridium 192	78 **Pt** platinum 195	79 **Au** gold 197	80 **Hg** mercury 201	81 **Tl** thallium 204	82 **Pb** lead 207	83 **Bi** bismuth 209	84 **Po** polonium 209	85 **At** astatine 210	86 **Rn** radon 222
87 **Fr** francium 223	88 **Ra** radium 226	89 **Ac** actinium 227	104 **Rf** rutherfordium 261	105 **Db** dubnium 262	106 **Sg** seaborgium 266	107 **Bh** bohrium 264	108 **Hs** hassium 269	109 **Mt** meitnerium 268	110 **Ds** darmstadtium 271	111 **Rg** roentgenium 272	112 **Uub** ununbium 285	113 **Uut** ununtrium 284	114 **Uuq** ununquadium 289	115 **Uup** ununpentium 288	116 **Uuh** ununhexium 292		

Lanthanides:

58 **Ce** cerium 140	59 **Pr** praseodymium 141	60 **Nd** neodymium 144	61 **Pm** promethium 145	62 **Sm** samarium 150	63 **Eu** europium 152	64 **Gd** gadolinium 157	65 **Tb** terbium 159	66 **Dy** dysprosium 163	67 **Ho** holmium 165	68 **Er** erbium 167	69 **Tm** thulium 169	70 **Yb** ytterbium 173	71 **Lu** lutetium 175

Actinides:

90 **Th** thorium 232	91 **Pa** protactinium 231	92 **U** uranium 238	93 **Np** neptunium 237	94 **Pu** plutonium 244	95 **Am** americium 243	96 **Cm** curium 247	97 **Bk** berkelium 247	98 **Cf** californium 251	99 **Es** einsteinium 252	100 **Fm** fermium 257	101 **Md** mendelevium 258	102 **No** nobelium 259	103 **Lr** lawrencium 262

Index